CARE OF THE COMPETITION HORSE

CARE OF THE COMPETITION HORSE

Sarah Pilliner

B.T. Batsford Ltd · London

First published 1994

© Sarah Pilliner 1994

Typeset by Servis Filmsetting Ltd, Manchester
and printed in Great Britain by Butler and
Tanner, Frome, Somerset

Published by
B.T. Batsford Ltd
4 Fitzhardinge Street
London W1H 0AH

A CIP catalogue record for this book is available
from the British Library

ISBN 0 7134 7090 9

CONTENTS

ACKNOWLEDGEMENTS

The author would like to thank Sarah Cotton for her unstinting support, without her inspiration a clear round cross country at Osberton would not have been possible. Thanks are also due to Blackwells Scientific Publications for allowing the use of extracts from *Getting Horses Fit* and *Horse Nutrition and Feeding* both by Sarah Pilliner.

All technical line illustrations are by Carole Vincer, and the decorative line illustrations are by Gabrielle Ceriden Morse.

All photographs are by Joanna Prestwich, except **9** and **10** by Christie Lomax, and **21**, **32** and **33** by Kit Houghton.

INTRODUCTION

The equine industry

Far from being a relic of a bygone age or a charming anachronism, the horse contributes significantly to the economies of the UK and USA. Most of the horse's former tasks have been taken over by the internal combustion engine, but there are as many horses in Britain today as there were in Victorian times. This has been due to the growth of the racing industry and the higher living standards that have allowed families to own or have access to horses – once a prerogative of the wealthy. The equine industry also provides revenue for many other sectors, including those involving textiles, clothing, engineering, pharmaceuticals, publishing and journalism.

In the UK alone, for example, there are an estimated 600,000 horses and ponies, ridden by a remarkable 3·3 million people more than twice a month. The British equine industry provides full-time employment for nearly 100,000 people with an annual turnover in the region of £800 million, placing it in the same category as the office-machinery sector or the record industry. This turnover does not include the revenue from betting duty, which in 1990 brought in £459 million.

Horse sports

Much of the success of the equine industry is due to the rise in popularity of the competition horse. Horses have been used for competition for thousands of years, but horse competition as we know it today is a development of the twentieth century, with massive growth in the last thirty years. Riding for leisure and in competition, and with it the breeding, production and care of competition horses, has become a specialized industry.

The oldest equestrian sport still being practised today is probably polo, with other sports, such as eventing, dressage, show jumping, endurance, driving, hunting, showing, racing, Western riding, team chasing, vaulting and gymkhana, all having their enthusiastic followers.

The current Olympic disciplines are three-day eventing, dressage and show jumping, but the Equestrian World Games also include endurance riding, driving and vaulting. Western riding and its associated sports has yet to make much of an impact outside the USA, but is a huge part of the American horse industry.

As horse sports become more popular it is important that riders understand how to care for the competition horse.

Care of the competition horse

It is quite probable that a horse will be the third most expensive item (after your house and car) that you ever buy, but, unlike a car, a horse cannot go to the garage for a new engine should the old one burn out due to neglect. It is vitally important that this new member of your family receives the care and attention that is morally due a living creature. You also have your investment to protect, as you cannot cut corners and expect a horse to mature into a valuable athlete which is able to perform successfully.

The information in this book will help you to design individual training programmes to get your horse fit before competition, and to keep him fit throughout the competition season. Training is only one aspect of preparing the successful competition horse, however, and careful consideration must also be given to his feeding and to your stable-management regime. Having arrived at a competition, the horse must be treated correctly before, during and after his work if he is to compete happily and stay sound and healthy for this and future seasons; this includes considerate travelling and thoughtful warming-up and cooling-down procedures. In this way you can give your horse every chance to fulfil his potential, while all that you have left to do is to make sure that you are fit and trained enough to live up to your horse!

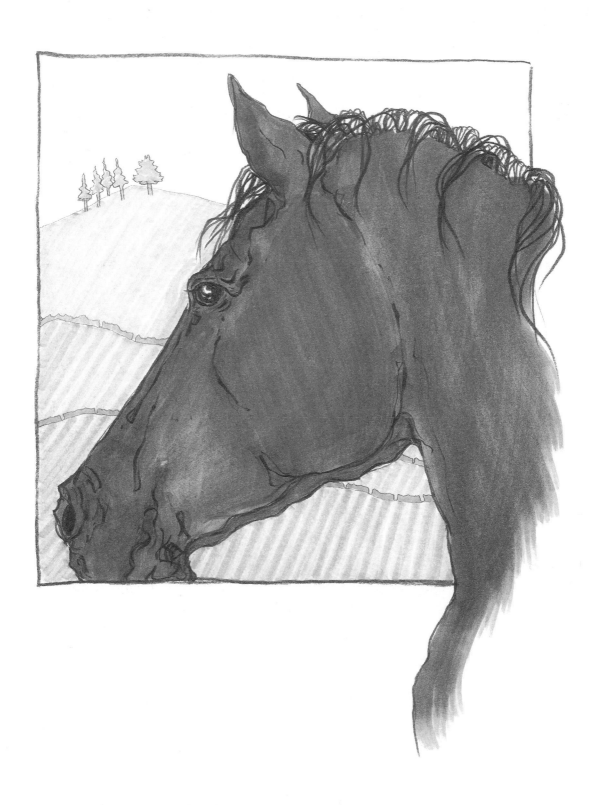

Part 1
PREPARATION OF THE COMPETITION HORSE

1
GETTING THE COMPETITION HORSE FIT

The aim of a fitness programme is to produce a horse that is 'fit', or, in other words, in a state suitable for carrying out the work required without over-stress. The level of fitness needed is dictated by the intensity of the effort the horse has to perform. A show jumper might be able to jump his Nations' Cup track without problems, for instance, but he would not be able to complete a three-day event without becoming distressed.

Getting a horse fit involves a mixture of correct work and a balanced, adequate diet. One without the other will not produce a horse capable of performing at his best. The basis of any fitness programme is to increase the horse's ability to tolerate work by gradually increasing his workload and energy intake. This slow, steady progression is fundamental to the physical and mental well-being of the horse, building confidence and security in his own ability.

The conventional methods have developed from getting hunters fit from grass. Traditionally, hunters are brought up from grass at the beginning of August, allowing three months to get them hunting fit, which is equivalent to one-day-event fitness or twenty-mile distance-ride fitness. This three-month period can be split into three four-week blocks: preliminary walking and trotting work, development work and fast work.

Getting the horse up from grass

At some point in the year, the competition horse will be roughed off and given a complete rest to allow him to unwind, mentally and physically. When this 'holiday' is taken will depend on the discipline in which the horse is competing: the hunter will rest during the summer months, for instance, while the event horse has his break in the winter. The routine for getting an unfit horse up from grass follows the same basic pattern, with some obvious differences.

Vaccinations

If the horse did not have his annual vaccination boosters before his holiday, they should be given before any work is begun. Check that the horse is vaccinated in accordance with current veterinary practice and as required by the rules of the competitions you intend to enter. In the UK competition, horses must be vaccin-

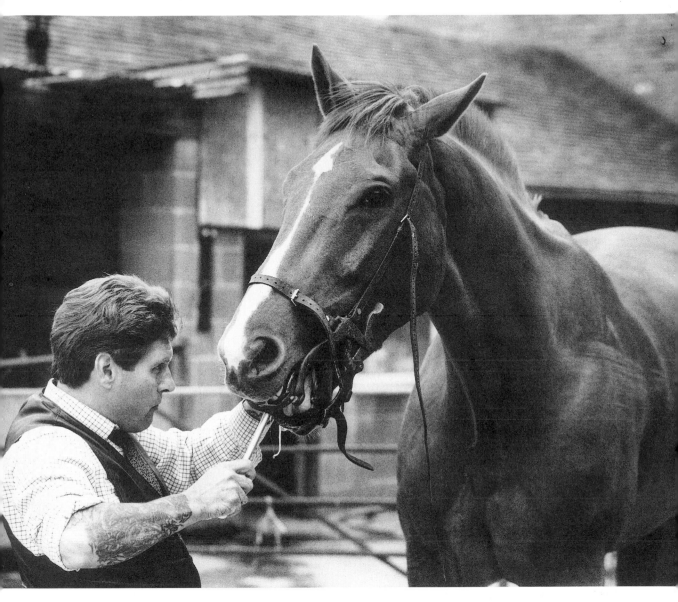

1 Rasping the horse's teeth, using a gag to keep the mouth open

ated against equine influenza and tetanus, and in the USA horses need to be vaccinated against Eastern and Western Encephalomyelitis. Horses travelling to competitions should be protected against rhinopneumonitis (EHV-1), rabies and potomac horse fever.

Make sure that the information is recorded correctly on the certificate and that the diagram of the horse is absolutely accurate. The horse will need seven days' light work after vaccination to minimize the risk of any adverse reaction.

Teeth

The horse's teeth are continually growing, and sharp or rough teeth can affect his condition and performance. A young horse may need wolf teeth removed, which will mean a rest period to allow healing. The vet or horse dentist should check the horse's teeth every six months. He will rasp or float the rough edges of the teeth, relieving any discomfort **(1)**.

Worming

An appropriate annual worming prog-ramme should be planned, with horses being wormed when they are first brought in, and then every four to six weeks. It is wise to avoid worming horses immediately before or after major competitions.

Shoeing

Horses must be shod all round once road work starts, and a heavier set of shoes will last longer during this initial fitness-developing period. Non-slip Tungsten nails are a good way of coping with slippery roads; road studs tend to unbalance the foot as it hits the ground. The horse should be shod every four to six weeks. If this is left too long, the foot becomes unbalanced, putting strain on joints, tendons and ligaments.

Equipment

The tack should have been stored in good condition at the end of the previous sea-son, with the stitching checked and saddle re-stuffed if necessary. The hard, fit horse that you last sat on will have become soft and probably fatter – saddles and girths may no longer fit, and poorly fitting tack will soon rub a soft horse's skin. A thick numnah (saddle pad) and a girth sleeve are a good idea to prevent rubbing and to absorb sweat, and must be washed regu-larly. Salt water or methylated spirits can also be applied to vulnerable areas to harden up the skin.

Trimming and bathing

The horse will have his mane, tail, heels and whiskers trimmed, depending on ind-ividual preference. If the weather is mild he can be washed to help rid the coat of parasites, grease and scurf.

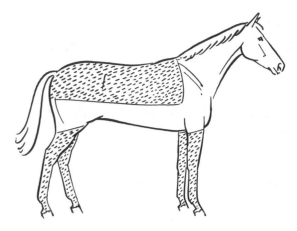

Fig. 1 Blanket clip: a useful clip while the horse is walking, as the loins are left covered for warmth

Fig. 2 Trace clip: so-called because it follows the line of the traces of carriage harness. This leaves additional protection on the neck

Fig. 3 Hunter clip: protection is left on the legs and saddle area

Clipping

If the horse is turned away during the winter, even with a New Zealand rug, he will have grown a winter coat and need clipping. A blanket or trace clip is quite adequate while the horse is walking (**figs 1 and 2**), but some people prefer to clip horses out as soon as walking commences (**fig. 3**). If so, it is important that horses are kept warm and dry on exercise, as walking does not produce much heat. Clipping the legs may improve a horse's appearance but will leave them with little protection against thorns and mud, and brushing boots will rub more easily. After clipping, extra rugs must be put on to keep the horse warm in the stable.

Blood tests

It is useful to have a blood test taken when the horse comes up from grass and to repeat this eight to ten weeks later. Blood tests can be used to detect ill-health and ascertain levels of fitness, but it is important to build up a blood profile for each horse and not just to carry out a one-off test (see page 36). All horses have different blood pictures at peak fitness.

Riding in winter

Watch out for black ice and try to ride later in the morning to give the ice time to melt. If you ride early or in rain or mist, when visibility is poor, it is wise to invest in reflective clothing. There are many suitable products on the market, ranging from quarter sheets and boots to hat covers and coats. They may not be the height of fashion, but they could prevent a serious accident. If the roads are snowy, packing the inside of the hoof with grease or a thick layer of oil will help to prevent snow from balling in the foot and help the

horse to keep his feet. A hoof pick is useful to clear the snow from the foot while on exercise.

Boots

As a general rule, the horse should be exercised in front boots and knee boots (**fig. 4**). Back boots can also be used if the horse's action makes them necessary. Knee boots should fit snugly above the knee while the bottom strap is done up loosely to allow room for the knee to flex. Normally exercise boots are lightweight with Velcro fastenings, if leather boots are used they must be kept clean and supple to avoid chafing the horse's legs.

Fig. 4 Exercise boots and knee boots suitable for walking work on the road. Note that the lower strap of the knee boot is loose to allow flexion of the knee

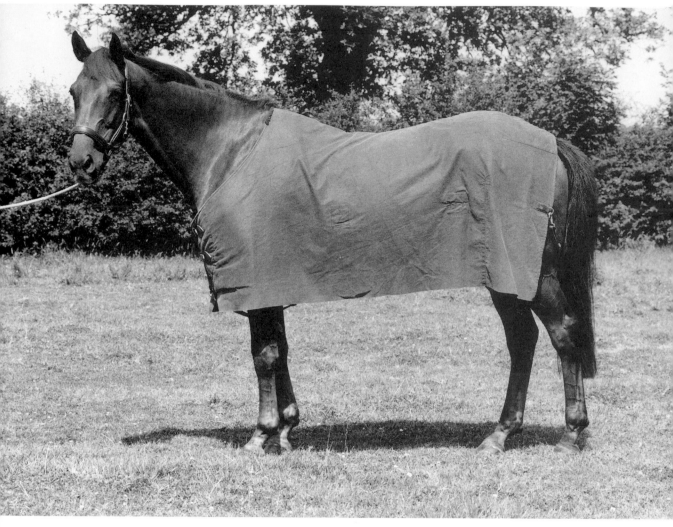

Turning out

The horse will benefit from being turned out in a New Zealand rug for a few hours every day, to help him unwind and stay sane **(2)** and **(3)**. He has been accustomed to being out for most of the day, and if part of his routine is a daily turn-out he is unlikely to have a wild fling and gallop about. If the weather is cold, a jute rug under his New Zealand will stop a wind chilling him as quickly, and a neck guard or hood will give additional warmth and save a lot of grooming time.

Horses turned out in muddy paddocks should be watched for mud fever on the legs. When washing off mud, rinse the legs

2 A well-fitting New Zealand rug should be of adequate length and depth, and must not slip back to sit on the horse's withers

in salt water and dry them with a clean towel or absorbent paper. A dusting of talcum powder will help to dry legs and is especially useful if bandages have to go on to damp legs.

In the summer, horses should be protected from flies, or they may become very frustrated and actually start to lose condition.

Protective net hoods can be attached to the headcollar to prevent flies irritating the horse's eyes. Fly spray or oil of citronella should be applied regularly.

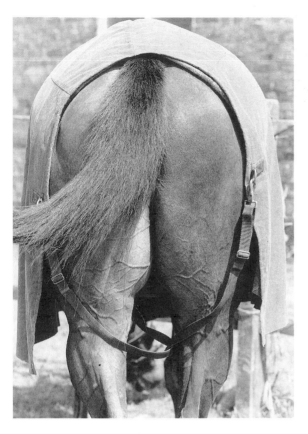

3 The leg straps of the New Zealand rug are crossed, and should not droop down by the hocks or ride up between the legs

Feeding

Some horses may only need grass and hay to maintain or improve their condition while they are on holiday, while others may need concentrates. The amount given will depend on each horse, the time of the year and the weather conditions, but is normally between 2–5 kg (4·5–11 lb) of feed a day.

If the horse has not been receiving any concentrate feed, a small feed of a low-energy food such as horse and pony cubes (pellets) should be fed in the field for the week before he is brought up. This will help his digestive system to adjust to the feed he will be given once stabled.

Preliminary work

The preliminary work is designed to exercise the horse slowly for increasing lengths of time to tone up the muscles, tendons and ligaments and to harden the soft horse's skin. The importance of the initial walking and trotting work that is carried out at this stage cannot be over-emphasized. Fitness is like a pyramid, and the broader the base, the higher the peak that can be reached.

Weeks 1 and 2: walking

The walking commences in one of the following ways.

1. The horse is walked for about twenty to thirty minutes a day, building up to an hour by the end of the first week and two hours by the end of the second week. The horse is turned out for the rest of the day. This 'half-and-half' system is good for the horse both physically and mentally.
2. The walking can be split into two periods a day, starting with about twenty minutes for each session and gradually building this up.
3. The horse has a short holiday of only two to four weeks, after which he is walked two or three times a week for up to an hour each time. This helps to maintain a basic level of fitness and to keep the tendons and bones strong. The risk of girth galls and a sore back is also lessened. Once the horse starts to walk every day, he can have sixty minutes' exercise.

Walking can become very boring and the weather may be cold and unpleasant, but the horse should always be walked on the bit or on a long rein, never on a loose floppy rein, which is bad discipline for

Fig. 5 Correctly executed road work. Both horse and rider are suitably dressed, and the horse is attentive, balanced and active

Weeks 3 and 4: trotting

After the initial walking work, trot can be introduced; this can be alternated between roads and grass or in an arena. A certain amount of trotting on the road will help the horse to cope with hard ground, but too much will cause concussion and jarring.

Initially, the trot should only be for two or three minutes at a time, building up over the next couple of weeks to fifteen minutes in total, split into three or four periods, depending on the terrain. If the trotting is done in an arena, sharp turns and small circles must be avoided at this stage. Flat work can be incorporated into the routine towards the end of the fourth week; this should be no more than thirty minutes before or after an hour's road work. As the horse becomes fitter, lunge work can begin; twenty minutes twice a week is probably enough. Work on the lunge in side reins can be very strenuous for young horses and should not be over-used until the horse is fitter **(fig. 6)**.

Feeding

If the horse is confined to his stable and his only exercise is when ridden, he may turn into a bucking bronco and the concentrate feed must be cut. It is far better to under-feed than over-feed the concentrates at this stage, but a lot of hay (or its dust-free equivalent) must be fed to prevent the stabled horse from becoming bored. (See pages 47–49 for further advice on feeding.) It may be advisable to split the work into two sessions or to do a little trotting on unpoached ground if the horse cannot be turned out and is getting above himself. During this period it is wise to avoid high energy feeds; horse and pony cubes or mix fed with chaff and sugar beet pulp would be sufficient. Oats, barley and high energy cubes or mixes can be introduced at the next stage of training.

both horse and rider **(fig. 5)**. A horse walker can be used to do the majority of his walking work, or he can be led from another horse. The disadvantage is that these methods will not accustom the back muscles to carrying a rider, and the girth region will remain soft.

Ideally, the horse should be walked on the roads for up to two hours a day for four weeks and never for less than two weeks. The longer the holiday, the more road work will be needed. If the horse has been walked two or three times a week from the field, another two weeks on top should suffice once he has come in.

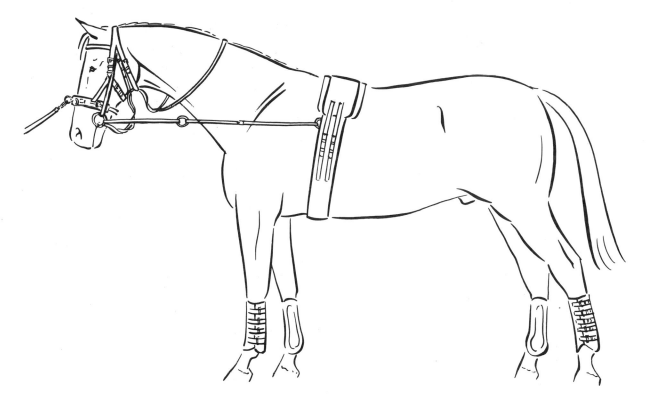

Fig. 6 A horse tacked up for lungeing, with side reins attached to the surcingle

Development work

The horse should by now be ready to progress to the next stage of training, with the introduction of canter work and suppling exercises. Development work will vary according to the discipline for which the horse is being prepared, but the principle is to begin to work the horse harder so that the heart and lungs become accustomed to exercise. This gradually builds up the horse's stamina, while the muscles continue to strengthen and adapt to the work that the horse is being given.

The ground chosen for the first canter should be suitable; the overexuberant horse will often want to go faster than his rider. It may be wise to use the manege as this is an environment that the horse associates with discipline and the surface will not overstress his limbs. Canter work should be slow and short initially, avoiding tight turns and circles.

Fast work

The third period of the fitness programme is even more specialized. The power and athleticism of the dressage horse and show jumper are developed further, while the racehorse and the event horse are given fast work. Some horses, such as ridden show horses, for example, never embark on this third stage, but would continue to build up body, skin and coat condition and become more highly trained.

Fast work should be carried out on gallops or in a suitable field taking care that the ground is not soft or rutted; many instances of lameness occur as the galloping horse hits a piece of bad ground. The horse must always be thoroughly warmed up and cooled down, particularly if he has been transported to the area of work.

Interval training

Interval training was originally developed to train middle- and long-distance runners and swimmers, and has been used successfully in human athletics for over twenty years. Interval training has been adapted for event horses and used by top British and American event riders, and this has led to a great deal of interest in this method of training among riders at all levels of the horse-trials world.

Interval training cannot cut corners, nor will it allow a beginner to get a horse three-day-event fit from a book. It does, however, help the less-experienced rider to get a horse fit, rather than relying on that indefinable quality of 'feel', which only comes with years of practice in training horses.

Interval training consists of giving a horse a period of specific work (canter) followed by a brief interval of semi-rest (walk), during which the horse is allowed to recover partially before being asked to work again.

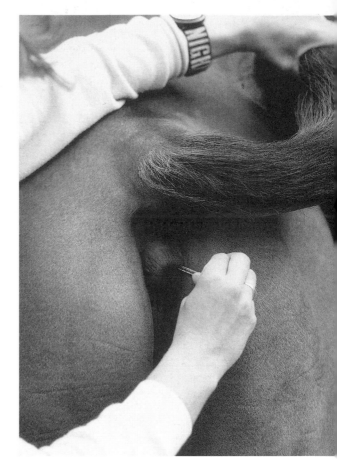

4 Taking the horse's rectal temperature

5 Taking the horse's pulse at the facial artery

The aims of interval training

A fit event horse or long-distance horse is one which has a greater capacity for using oxygen and performing aerobic work; the point at which anaerobic work starts is delayed as much as possible so that the resultant lactic-acid build-up is also postponed. This results in the horse being able to work for longer before fatigue sets in.

The periods of work given during interval training develop and extend the horse's capacity for intensive work as the programme progresses, without a build-up of lactic acid – a major factor contributing to fatigue – because the walking periods between canters allow the blood to remove any lactic acid that may be building up in the muscle. Interval training increases the horse's tolerance to stress, and the measurement of pulse, respiration and recovery rates means that the horse's reaction to the training programme can be closely monitored.

One of the reasons that interval training appears to be successful is that the monitoring of the horses vital signs means that the less experienced rider is less likely to over stress the horse and yet ensures that the horse is worked hard enough to attain the desired level of fitness.

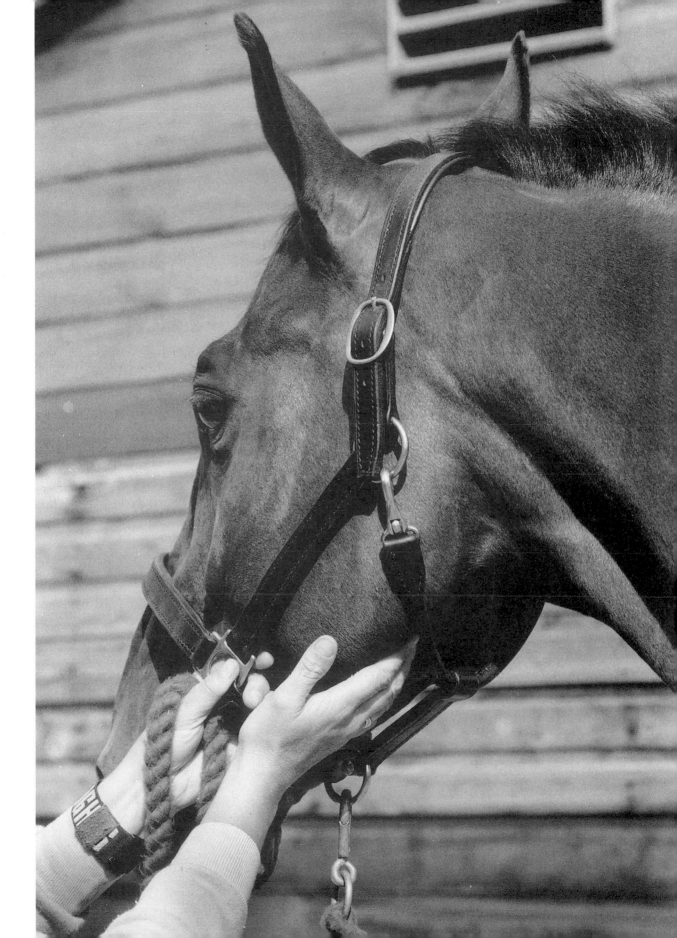

Monitoring interval training

Monitoring the horse's temperature, pulse and respiration (T.P.R.) is an essential part of the interval-training regime. The horse cannot tell the rider how he feels, and so the rider must learn to read the signs of stress.

Temperature The horse's normal resting temperature is 38°C (100–1°F). Any deviation from the normal temperature may indicate stress of some sort, most commonly illness. A clean veterinary thermometer, lightly greased with vaseline, is used to take a horse's rectal temperature (see **4** on page **20**). Standing to one side of the horse's hindquarters, lift the tail and gently insert the thermometer in the rectum with a twisting action. Place the thermometer full-length into the rectum, pressing it gently against the wall of the rectum for one to two minutes. Remove the thermometer slowly with a rotating move-

ment and read. Digital-read-out thermometers, although more expensive, are easy to read and a useful addition to the first-aid kit.

Pulse The horse's normal resting pulse rate is 36–42 beats per minute (b.p.m.), and corresponds to the horse's heart rate. The easiest place to take the horse's pulse is where the facial artery runs over the cheek bone (see **5** on the previous page); run the fingers down the inside of the horse's left cheek bone until you feel a moveable lump, about the diameter of a pencil, running across the bone. Gently press the first two fingers along this lump, cupping the cheek bone, and count the pulse for ten seconds, multiplying by six to calculate the pulse rate per minute.

A stethoscope can also be used on the left side of the horse, just behind the elbow, in front of the girth (**fig. 7**). The mounted rider can lean down and press the back of his or her ungloved hand against the horse in front of the girth. Once the horse has had a canter the heart will be clearly felt hammering against the ribs!

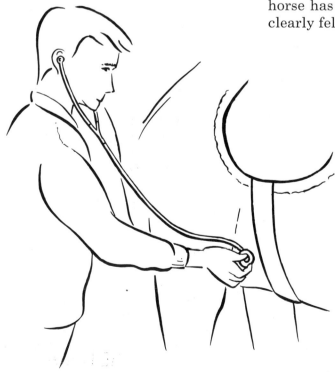

Fig. 7 Using a stethoscope to monitor the horse's heart rate

Fig. 8 Calculating the horse's respiration rate by observing the rise and fall of the flanks

Respiratory rate The horse's normal resting breathing rate – how often he breathes in and out – is 8–16 breaths per minute. To take the respiration rate, observe the in-and-out motion of the ribs or rise and fall of the flanks **(fig. 8)**. Each combination of in and out is counted as one. The rider can also put a hand close to the horse's nostril and count as the horse breathes out – beware that the horse does not sniff your hand looking for titbits! In cold weather the horse's breath can be seen as he breathes out.

To obtain 'normal' values, each of these measurements should be taken while the horse is calm and at rest; for example, between feeding and the daily exercise. These values are then used as a baseline against which the values after exercise can be compared.

BEFORE STARTING

Interval training cannot cut corners, and the following factors must be considered before starting a programme.

- The horse should be capable of ninety minutes' walk and trot over rolling terrain without distress. The horse conditioned slowly and carefully will stay in peak condition longer than one pushed too fast in the early stages.
- It is essential to keep a notebook with a running record of the horse's response to work, and to adjust the programme accordingly. As well as the T.P.R., the weather, type of work and how the horse 'feels' should also be noted. The weather can have a profound effect on how quickly the horse recovers from work. During hot and humid weather the horse will continue breathing fast for longer than expected, as more rapid breathing is necessary to reduce body heat, so – even though the pulse rate may drop to normal – the horse's breathing may still be fast. Pulse is a more reliable gauge of the horse's recovery and fitness, and is the most important reading (See (5) on page 21).
- As in any form of training, the rider must be alert to any change in the horse's attitude, appetite, coat, droppings, appearance, muscle tone, etc.
- Interval training may not suit all horses. Youngsters may not be mentally or physically ready to cope with a rigorous training schedule, for instance. Some excitable horses seem to settle into canter work-outs, making them easier to hold when competing, while lazy horses become bored with interval training.
- The breeding, condition and previous training must also be considered. A stuffy horse may need to work up to a different end point, so that he is fitter than the more athletic, thoroughbred-type horse.
- Any past soundness problems and the amount of time the horse has had off must be taken into consideration when designing the training programme.

How to use interval training

During exercise, the horse's pulse and respiration rates increase – just as yours do. During interval training the horse is cantered at a pre-determined speed for a certain time. After this piece of work, the horse is pulled up and the pulse and/or respiration rates recorded immediately, and then the horse is walked for a set time and the rates recorded again. The difference between the two readings is the 'recovery rate' of the horse.

The horse repeats these work-outs every four days and the pulse and respiration rates are recorded at the same points; as the horse gets fitter, he will recover faster from the work. Fitness is gradually built up by slowly adding to the amount of work the horse is asked to do, by increasing the speed and/or length of the work-out or by using more demanding terrain. If the recovery rate is not good enough after a work-out, the work is adjusted so that the horse is never over-stressed.

The trainer or rider should know the horse and understand his capabilities and limitations, and be aware of the degree of fitness that is eventually required, so that a flexible programme can be made to suit any horse. This system is markedly different from the more traditional methods, where horses are trotted and cantered for long distances with short, sharp gallops later in the training programme and no repetition of fast work in each work-out. If the horse is not responding to the programme as desired then the rider can change the speed, duration, number of repetitions or the time between the work-outs. For example if a horse is still blowing he could be allowed to walk for another minute before cantering again. Alternatively if the horse has recovered well the time between canters could be cut by a minute.

The method

In order to carry out interval training correctly, a *known distance* should be covered in a *set time*. Ideally, 1,600 metres (one mile) should marked off in 400-metre ($\frac{1}{4}$ mile) segments, but if this is not possible, a 400-metre gallop will be adequate as long as there are no sharp turns. An easy-to-read wrist stop-watch makes life much easier!

The time allowed for covering this distance can be calculated according to the competition for which the horse is being trained.

- 400 metres in one minute 49 seconds is 220 metres per minute (m.p.m.), which is the good on-going trot required for phases A and C (roads and tracks) of a three-day event. This is about 13 kilometres per hour (9 m.p.h.).
- 400 metres in one minute is 400 m.p.m. – a brisk canter – which is a good basis for canter work.
- 400 metres in 46 seconds is 520 m.p.m., the Novice cross-country speed.
- 400 metres in 35 seconds is 690 m.p.m., the Advanced three-day-event steeplechase speed.

It is important for the event rider and the long-distance rider to be able to pace his or her horse over a given distance and different ground during competition, and interval training helps the rider to do this early on in the training programme. It also means that the horse is used to travelling at the required speed, which is useful during competition. In order to design an effective training programme, the rider needs to know exactly what is required in competition in terms of speed, distance, length and intensity, so that these aspects can be incorporated into the training programme.

The relevant rule book should be consulted for up to date times, speeds and distances.

Fig. 9 In interval training, the amount and speed of canter work are built up in gradual stages

If the rider is not experienced in using interval training, it is best to start the canter work very gradually **(fig. 9)**. After an initial twenty-minute warm-up period of walking and trotting, the measured 400-metre distance should be cantered in one minute (400 m.p.m.). This is followed by three minutes' walking and another one-minute canter, after which the pulse and respiration rates are recorded. If after ten minutes' walking the pulse has returned to normal, the horse can work harder in his next canter session, four days later. The horse's pulse and respiration values will rarely return to the resting values obtained in the stable, due to excitement and the fact that he is recovering in walk, so a value for the horse's warmed-up pulse and respiration should be obtained and used as baseline values. A horse walking actively will have a heart rate of 60–70 beats per minute.

During the next canter work-out, the horse can be cantered for three minutes at 400 m.p.m., followed by one minute in trot and a recovery period in walk of three to five minutes. This is repeated twice, after which the horse is cooled down in walk for at least twenty minutes.

The heart rate should be no more than 150 beats per minute at the end of each canter, and no more than 100 b.p.m. before the next canter commences. If the heart rate takes more than five minutes to drop below 100 b.p.m., the canter was too long, the terrain too steep, the speed too fast or the initial work has not been carried out correctly.

The canter work is built up gradually until the horse has reached the desired fitness. The flexibility of interval training means that it can be used to get horses as diverse as event horses and long-distance horses fit very effectively.

Training the event horse

In body condition, eventers lie between racehorses and show jumpers or dressage horses. Being a 'jack of all trades' – distance, speed, power and control – he has to compromise. He must be fast enough to gallop cross-country within the time without distress, and yet he needs to combine this with other talents and physical demands. He is therefore not as lean and wiry as the National Hunt horse, but is less well-covered than the dressage horse – he must avoid the strain of too much weight on his limbs and wind, and yet the dressage demands muscular development of the neck and back.

The event horse has to gallop in a balanced, calm manner and in a round outline; he must be able to lengthen and shorten his stride and to cope with gradients while carrying the rider's weight. Many horses find this difficult and have to be taught to gallop – the stuffy, short-striding horse is a prime example, and he may have to be worked more strongly than his longer-striding counterpart.

Big, long-striding horses will sometimes need to be worked more slowly to keep them calm and balanced. A reluctant or lazy horse may benefit from galloping alongside another horse; this will teach him to enjoy galloping and make him try harder.

POINTS TO REMEMBER

- Interval training must be monitored by pulse and respiration rate, not by time alone. It is the pulse rate immediately after the work which shows the level of stress to which the horse has been subjected, and the recovery rate which shows how fit he is. Without these records, interval training is meaningless and can actually be harmful.
- If the horse is required to work anaerobically, the pulse rate should exceed 200 beats per minute; this can be estimated by checking the pulse one minute after pulling up. If the horse has been beneficially stressed, his pulse will lie between 120–150 b.p.m. one minute after stopping work. If it is greater than 150 b.p.m., he has been over-stressed; if it is less than 120 b.p.m., he has not worked hard enough. This guide should only be used well into the programme or the horse may be over-worked.
- If the pulse and respiration have not returned to normal within twenty minutes of completing the work-out, the horse has been over-worked and the programme should be adapted accordingly.
- The respiration rate should not exceed the pulse rate. If it does, stop work and ascertain what has caused this: lack of fitness, environmental conditions or a problem with the horse's respiratory tract?
- Never finish the work if the horse is distressed: gasping, blowing excessively, stumbling, changing legs frequently and showing reluctance to continue.
- On the other hand, the horse must be stressed enough to stimulate the body systems to become better adapted to exercise. The heart rate must be raised above 100 b.p.m. after work.
- It is possible to over-train horses. If the horse is getting too fit too quickly, increase the distance of the canter rather than the speed. Long, slow work for a couple of sessions will maintain fitness without exciting the horse.
- The programme should be planned backwards from the proposed competition(s), so that work days fall into appropriate places before competition.
- Always warm up and cool down thoroughly before cantering, particularly if the horse has to travel in a lorry or trailer to the work area.

When to start

It is wise to get the event horse up from his winter break in December rather than in January, as, if the programme does not begin until after Christmas and the weather turns icy and snowy, there may not be enough time to do the road work thoroughly.

The exercise programme

You must allow three months to prepare for the first event of the season, bearing in mind that show jumping, dressage and cross-country competitions may be part of the build-up. To achieve basic fitness, the programme outlined on pages 17–18 should be used: two weeks of walking work, followed by two weeks of walking and trotting.

The one-day-event horse

The following programme assumes that the horse has been turned out during the day, stabled at night and fed two concentrate feeds a day, with hay at night, and is in good condition. The basic preliminary work is as has already been outlined, but the subsequent development and fast work are specialized.

The one day event horse has to perform a dressage test and a show jumping round requiring obedience and accuracy. He is then asked to gallop round a cross country course consisting of fixed, solid obstacles. The degree of difficulty of the questions asked the horse depend on the grade in which he is competing; horses gain points for winning or being placed and at a set number of points move up to the next grade. Thus the degree of fitness and training required will increase as the horse progresses up the horse trials ladder.

Weeks 5–6: cantering

The initial canter work may be carried out in a schooling environment, where horses feel a sense of discipline and often respect their riders more than in an open space. The horse should be cantered for two to three minutes at 400 m.p.m. at first, and brought back to walk through trot. These little bouts of canter are built up so that, by the end of two weeks, the horse is cantering for a total of nine to ten minutes, split into three or four sessions. Always walk the horse for between two and five minutes after each canter.

During week five or six, jumping can be introduced into the training programme, starting with pole work, grid work and small jumps in the school. The jumping can be incorporated into the schooling programme so that, by the end of the second month, the novice horse should have competed in a small local show-jumping class or two.

Weeks 7–10: interval training

By the end of week six, the horse will have been cantering for at least one week, and interval training can start in earnest. Canter work is repeated every fourth day, with the sessions built up minute by minute. The day after a canter session should be a rest, or just a hack for one-and-a-half to two hours. Over the next two weeks, the sessions are built up so that the horse can complete three five-minute canters at 400 m.p.m., with three minutes' walking in between, as shown in Table 1 (see overleaf).

It is wise to replace front brushing boots with tendon-support boots for canter work and jump training, to avoid injury by the horse striking into his front legs from behind (**fig. 10**, overleaf). If over-reach boots are used, make sure that they are not floppy, risking the horse treading on them

6 A rubber over-reach or bell boot. The boot should just clear the ground when the horse is standing still. If it is too large, the excess can be trimmed off

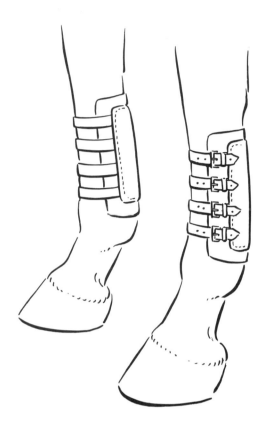

Fig. 10 Open-fronted tendon-support boots

with his hind feet **(6)**. The heavier shoes used for road work should by now have been replaced by lighter ones, fitted with stud holes ready for future events.

By now the horse will have been in for about ten weeks. Road work continues each day, with forty-five minutes on canter days and one-and-a-half to two hours on hack-only days.

Weeks 10–12: the final two weeks

The first horse trial can be planned for week twelve. In the final two weeks, the road work, schooling and jump training continue as usual. After one or two of these work sessions, the last minute of the last canter can be increased to a speed of 500 m.p.m.

The canter work is shown in Table 1.

Table 1 **Interval training to Novice one-day-event fitness**
20 minutes' warm-up
Canter 1: 5 minutes at 400 m.p.m.
trot 30 seconds
walk 3 minutes
Canter 2: 4 minutes at 400 m.p.m.
1 minute at 500 m.p.m.
trot 30 seconds to 1 minute
walk 3 minutes
Canter 3: 4 minutes at 400 m.p.m.
1 minute at 500 m.p.m., building up to 550 m.p.m.
trot 1 to 2 minutes
walk at least 20 minutes
The heart rate after the third canter should drop below 100 b.p.m. after 10 minutes' walking.

The idea of interval training is to allow the horse to work aerobically for longer periods. At some stage during the cross-country or steeplechase, however, the horse will work anaerobically. Increasing the speed at the end of the last two canter sessions, as shown in Table 1, makes the horse work anaerobically, and the trotting afterwards helps to disperse the lactic acid so that the heart rate recovers more quickly. Seven to ten days before the competition, take the horse cross-country schooling or to a Hunter Trial (this will replace a work day).

It cannot be emphasized enough that all horses are individuals and must be treated as such. Tables are merely a guideline and do not allow for lost shoes, heavy going or lazy horses. The real skill in training lies in the ability to design programmes for individual horses and to recognize the need to adapt the programme without hindering the horse's progress. The same programme may take up to two weeks longer with a different horse.

This sort of training should not be carried out more than twice a week. If a horse is experiencing difficulty, there are several factors which can be altered to suit the individual. These are: the distance of each canter; the speed; the interval between canters; and the number of canters. The training area will also vary with changes in the weather, so the rider must be prepared to alter the canter programme to allow for this.

Competing in horse trials

Ideally, horses should run every other weekend, and do no more than three horse trials on consecutive weekends. After each competition the horse should have a day off, followed by an easy day. If he is running on consecutive weekends, the horse should do a shorter piece of work

four days after the last competition. Two four-minute canters at 400 m.p.m., with a three-minute walk in-between, are probably sufficient.

It is important to allow enough time between competitions to iron out any problems which may have arisen with the young horse during competition. After about three months of competition, it is a good idea to give the young horse a short break and let him down a little; this will stop him becoming sour or jaded, and may coincide with mid-summer when the ground is at its hardest. The length of this mini-holiday will vary from horse to horse: two weeks out at grass by day and in at night with perhaps twenty minutes' lungeing a day may be enough.

After this break the horse should have two weeks' training and schooling before competing again. By this stage the rider should be aiming to be placed in competition. After another three months of competition, the horse should be roughed off for two months' rest or partial rest. It is important to give the horse concentrate feed during this period so that he does not lose condition.

The Novice's eventing year therefore looks like this, depending on the events for which he is entered:

January–March – getting fit

April/May/June – competing

Early July – rest

Late July – regaining fitness

August/Sept/Oct – competing

November/December – roughed off

Depending on how the horse fares and how many events he does, it may be beneficial to enter show jumping and dressage competitions during the year. These are useful during the run up to the season so that the horse is in tune at his first event.

Interval training to Advanced levels

The demands made upon horses which compete in three-day events require the horse to be at peak physical fitness and condition, and the rider and trainer must be aware of the rigorous task for which they are training the horse. On the cross-country day of a three-day event the horse will have to complete four phases, as outlined below.

Phases A and C: roads and tracks

Between 15,400 to 18,700 m (9·5 to 11·5 miles), to be covered at a speed of 220 m.p.m. This is a good working trot or mixture of walk and canter, aiming to cover one kilometre ($\frac{5}{8}$ mile) in four minutes, a total of 70 to 85 minutes of endurance-type work.

Phase B: steeplechase

Either 3,105 or 3,450 m (two miles) to be covered in either four-and-a-half or five minutes at a speed of 690 m.p.m. This is a fast gallop and the horse must be taught to jump safely at speed; if he is pushed out of his natural galloping stride he may fall or become tired during this phase.

Phase D: cross-country

Between 6,840 and 7,980 m (4 to 5 miles) to be covered at 570 m.p.m. in a time of between twelve and fourteen minutes. This is a fairly fast gallop, including up to forty-five jumping efforts over solid and imposing obstacles.

(Information taken from the BHS Horse Trials Rule Book 1992, for four-star three-day events.)

Many consider three-day events to be the ultimate test.

The aim of the training programme is for the horse to complete this severe test at the required speed without fatigue in the latter stages, which could lead to a silly mistake and a fall. The horse must also be fit enough to pass the veterinary inspection the next day and jump accurately.

The horse trained to Advanced one-day-event fitness (see Table 2) should be able to work aerobically during canters of up to 500 m.p.m. Cantering for longer periods does not actually increase the horse's ability to cope with the demands of the faster speeds in Advanced horse trials and three-day events. This means that the speed and/or hill work must be used to train horses at these levels; this is particularly so for part-bred horses. Before a rider attempts to get a horse to this level of fitness, he needs to know the horse intimately and to have a thorough knowledge of his requirements, capabilities and limitations. The breeding or type of horse, his present condition and previous fitness must all be considered when devising a horse's training programme.

It is generally accepted that it takes four months to get a horse from soft condition to three-day-event fitness. The task is made much easier if the following points are considered:

- the horse must be given concentrate feed while at grass
- if the weather is unpleasant or the ground wet, the horse should be stabled at night
- the break should not be too long; two months are enough to rest the horse, without the loss of too much fitness
- if the horse has not been brought to this level of fitness before, as much as four weeks may need to be added to the training programme
- the horse should have any soundness problems sorted out before being turned away

The first six weeks would be much as outlined for the Novice horse (see pages 32–33); the next four to six weeks would see the work being stepped up to get the horse to Advanced one-day-event fitness, as shown in Table 2.

Table 2 **Interval training to Advanced one-day-event fitness**

20 minutes' warm-up
Canter 1: 6 minutes at 450 m.p.m.
trot 30 seconds
walk 3 minutes
Canter 2: 4 minutes at 450 m.p.m.
3 minutes at 500 m.p.m.
trot 30 seconds to 1 minute
walk 3 minutes
Canter 3: 4 minutes at 450 m.p.m.
3 minutes at 500 m.p.m.,
building up to 600 m.p.m.
trot 1 to 2 minutes
walk at least 20 minutes

Generally speaking the older Advanced horse is easier to get fit than his younger Novice counterpart; his body systems have developed as the years go by and short breaks do not affect this deep fitness too adversely. For example as muscles are asked to perform more work, they demand a greater supply of nutrients such as oxygen. Oxygen is brought to the muscle in the bloodstream, so the body responds by developing the blood supply to the muscles, a process called capillarization. Realising the full potential of this development may take up to three years and while prolonged inactivity will cause these blood capillaries to 'dry up', the event horses' two month holiday should pose no problems. Similarly his respiratory system, muscles and bones will all be primed and ready to return to fitness more rapidly.

For the four to six weeks prior to a four-star three-day event such as Badminton or Burghley, the speed and length of the fast work in Table 2 would be gradually increased so that the last minute was performed at steeplechase speed (690 m.p.m.), to prepare the horse to travel the required distance at that speed. The length of the gallop is kept down to 690 metres (less than half a mile), so that the horse is not over-stressed but the body systems are primed to cope with anaerobic work. The final levels that riders work up to will vary. Some examples are given below.

- three repetitions of nine-minute canters at 550 m.p.m., two minutes' walking between each, with the last minute of the final two canters at 690 m.p.m.
- three repetitions of ten-minute canters at 550 m.p.m., three minutes' walking between each, with one full-speed 800 m ($\frac{1}{2}$ mile) gallop at the end.
- some riders believe that three repetitions of eight-minute canters are adequate, and that increasing to ten minutes does not significantly increase fitness, provided that the canters are fast enough.

The short sprints develop speed and strength while the long, slower canters develop rhythm and staying power. During racing and three-day eventing, maximum muscle contraction will be demanded and lactic acid will accumulate in the muscles. The horse's body must learn to cope with and dissipate these high lactate levels, so it really is important that these levels of exercise are experienced in training – hence the importance of the short gallop at the end of the canter work-out.

The length of time a horse blows after a work out will indicate the amount of anaerobic or maximal work the horse has done.

Table 3 **Interval training to Novice one-day-event fitness: a detailed 12-week schedule**

Throughout the programme, the horse should be turned out for a couple of hours whenever possible.

Week 1
Day 1: 20-minute walk
Day 2: 30-minute walk
Day 3: 40-minute walk
Day 4: 50-minute walk
Day 5: 60-minute walk
Day 6: 60-minute walk
Day 7: rest day

Week 2
Day 1: 1 hour 10-minute walk
Day 2: 1 hour 20-minute walk
Day 3: 1 hour 30-minute walk
Day 4: 1 hour 40-minute walk
Day 5: 1 hour 50-minute walk
Day 6: 2-hour walk
Day 7: rest day

Week 3
Day 1: 2-hour hack, including one 400 m (1 minute 49 second) trot
Day 2: 2-hour hack, including two 400 m trots
Day 3: 2-hour hack, including three 400 m trots
Day 4: 1 hour 30-minute hack, including two 800 m (3 minute 38 second) trots
Day 5: 1 hour 30-minute hack, including three 800 m trots, check recovery
Day 6: 1 hour 15-minute hack, including two 1100 m (5-minute) trots
Day 7: rest day

Week 4
Day 1: 1 hour 30-minute hack, including three 5-minute trots, check recovery
Day 2: as Day 1
Day 3: 60-minute walk plus 20 minutes' schooling
Day 4: as Day 1

Day 5: 60-minute walk plus 20 minutes' schooling
Day 6: as Day 1
Day 7: rest day

Week 5
Day 1: 1 hour 30-minute hack including three 5-minute trots and one 1-minute canter (400 m at 400 m.p.m.), check recovery. The canter work may be done in the school
Day 2: 60-minute walk plus 20 minutes' schooling, including pole work
Day 3: 60-minute walk plus 30 minutes' schooling
Day 4: 1 hour 30-minute hack, including three 5-minute trots and two 1-minute canters; check recovery
Day 5: 60-minute walk plus 30 minutes' schooling, including small jumps
Day 6: 1 hour 30-minute hack, including three 5-minute trots and three 1-minute canters, check recovery; *or* dressage competition
Day 7: rest day

Week 6
Day 1: 1 hour 30-minute hack, including three 5-minute trots and two 2-minute canters (800 m at 400 m.p.m.), check recovery
Day 2: 60-minute walk plus 40 minutes' schooling, including pole work
Day 3: 60-minute walk plus 40 minutes' schooling, including small jumps
Day 4: 1 hour 30-minute hack, including three 5-minute trots and three 2-minute canters; check recovery
Day 5: 60-minute walk plus 40 minutes' schooling
Day 6: 1 hour 30-minute hack, including three 5-minute trots and two 3-minute canters (1,200 m at 400 m.p.m.), check recovery; *or* small show-jumping competition
Day 7: rest day

Week 7
Interval training begins in earnest and the four-day schedule is adhered to as far as possible.

Day 1: hack

Day 2: 60-minute hack plus 40 minutes' schooling

Day 3: 60-minute hack plus 45 minutes' schooling and jumping

Day 4: 45-minute hack plus three 3-minute canters at 400 m.p.m. with 3-minute walk in-between, check recovery

Day 5: hack

Day 6: 60-minute hack plus 40 minutes' schooling

Day 7: dressage or show-jumping competition

Week 8

Day 1: 45-minute hack plus one 3-minute canter and two 4-minute canters at 400 m.p.m., with 3 minutes' walk in-between, check recovery

Day 2: rest day

Day 3: 60-minute hack plus 40 minutes' schooling

Day 4: 60-minute hack plus 45 minutes' schooling and jumping

Day 5: 45-minute hack plus three 4-minute canters at 400 m.p.m., with 3 minutes' walk in-between, check recovery

Day 6: hack

Day 7: 60-minute hack plus 40 minutes' schooling

Week 9

Day 1: 60-minute hack plus 45 minutes' schooling and jumping

Day 2: 45-minute hack plus two 4-minute and one 5-minute canters at 400 m.p.m., with 3 minutes' walk in-between, check recovery

Day 3: rest day

Day 4: 60-minute hack plus 40 minutes' schooling

Day 5: 60-minute hack plus 45 minutes' schooling and jumping

Day 6: 45-minute hack plus one 4-minute and two 5-minute canters at 400 m.p.m., with 3 minutes' walk in-between, check recovery

Day 7: hack

Week 10

Day 1: 60-minute hack plus 40 minutes' schooling

Day 2: 60-minute hack plus 45 minutes' schooling and jumping

Day 3: 45-minute hack plus three 5-minute canters at 400 m.p.m., with 3 minutes' walk in-between, check recovery

Day 4: rest day

Day 5: 60-minute hack plus 40 minutes' schooling

Day 6: 60-minute hack plus 45 minutes' schooling and jumping

Day 7: cross-country schooling to replace canter work

Week 11

Day 1: hack

Day 2: 60-minute hack plus 40 minutes' schooling

Day 3: 60-minute hack plus 45 minutes' schooling and jumping

Day 4: 45-minute hack plus one 5-minute canter at 400 m.p.m., two 4-minute canters at 400 m.p.m. finishing with 1 minute at 500 m.p.m., with 3 minutes' walk in-between, check recovery

Day 5: rest day

Day 6: 60-minute hack plus 40 minutes' schooling

Day 7: 60-minute hack plus 45 minutes' schooling and jumping

Week 12

Day 1: 45-minute hack plus one 5-minute canter at 400 m.p.m., one 4-minute canter at 400 m.p.m. plus 1 minute at 500 m.p.m., one 4-minute canter at 400 m.p.m. plus 1 minute at 550 m.p.m., with 3 minutes' walk in-between, check recovery

Day 2: hack

Day 3: 60-minute hack plus 40 minutes' schooling

Day 4: as day 3

Day 5: 60-minute hack plus 45 minutes' schooling and jumping

Day 6: FIRST HORSE TRIALS

Day 7: rest day

Training the endurance horse

Long-distance and endurance riding can cause severe distress in a horse which has not been properly prepared. The rider must also be fit. The rider must be able to recognize the smallest sign of over-stress in the horse and take immediate action. The horse may suffer muscular stress and start to flag and stumble, with muscle tremors in the flanks and thighs. If the pace is not steadied, the horse will become exhausted. Pulse rates will indicate cardio-vascular stress, while heatstroke, dehydration, azoturia or colic are symptoms of metabolic stress.

The long-distance horse will benefit from a longer period of slow work than the hunter. Some trainers advocate two months of walking and trotting, working up to three hours a day. Canter work is only introduced when stamina and muscle strength are well developed. Many riders do not have three hours a day to spend riding, however, and it is perfectly feasible to get a horse fit by riding him four days a week, with longer rides every weekend and plenty of time in the field (see Table 4).

There are now so many events throughout the season that it is possible to use thirty- and forty-mile competitive rides to work the horse's fitness up to the peak required for a hundred-mile ride. This may involve travelling fairly long distances, but the competitions have an advantage over long training rides from home, in that the horse works over more varied terrain. Less-experienced horses also become used to competing with others, and to standing quietly at the vetting when there are a lot of other horses around. It usually takes two or three years to build up to the fitness required for a hundred-mile ride.

Table 4 Training to endurance-ride fitness

November: rest
December: gentle exercise two or three times a week
January: 1–1½ hours, building up to 1½–2 hours (15 miles) four times a week
February: introduction of faster (not longer) rides of 25 miles at 7–8 m.p.h., using brisk rides and hills to raise the heart rate, not trotting long distances.
March/April: in Britain there is a 40-mile Golden Horseshoe qualifying ride every two to three weeks. The horse is inspected by a veterinary panel before the start of the ride, at the halfway halt and thirty minutes after the finish. A fit horse's pulse at the final vetting will have fallen to about 48 beats per minute: the highest allowed is 64 b.p.m., compared with a resting pulse rate of 36–42 b.p.m. If the horse is coping well with the rides, reduce work at home to 1–1½ hours' brisk work four times a week.
May: the Golden Horseshoe ride takes place in Britain: 100 miles in two days at 8 m.p.h. with no veterinary penalties. The horse should have one week off after this ride. Once the competition season is underway, the work that the horse is given at home needs only to be sufficient to keep him exercised and to prevent him from becoming bored.

STABLE-MANAGEMENT TIPS

- After each work-out, hose the horse's legs for five minutes and apply a cooling lotion or gel to help to get rid of any heat.
- As horses get fitter, they tend to eat less hay and will only eat a certain amount of concentrates, so feed to just below the horse's appetite so that he is always keen for his next meal. Make sure that he has the best-quality feed, and that any changes to the diet are made gradually.
- If in doubt, hay should be soaked or a dust-free alternative used. Shavings or paper make good alternatives to straw.

2
MONITORING FITNESS

How do you tell whether your horse is fit and healthy enough to compete? The monitoring of a horse's fitness is carried out at all levels, from the groom in the stable to the veterinary surgeon performing blood tests.

Good stable management

Temperature

We have already discussed the use of temperature, pulse and respiration values (T.P.R.) in assessing a horse's response to an interval-training programme. The T.P.R. is also equally valuable in a daily stable-management routine to check the horse's health.

A veterinary thermometer should be part of every grooming kit – it should not just be confined to the first-aid box – and the horse's temperature should be recorded daily. This allows you to be aware of each individual horse's 'normal' temperature (horses frequently and quite normally have a temperature 0·5–1 degree lower than what is officially denoted 'normal'). A slight fever is always an indicator that something is not quite

right, so if the horse has a higher than normal temperature, do not work him hard that day and watch for any further signs of illness.

Pulse and respiration rates

A knowledge of the horse's normal pulse and respiration rates will allow you to spot any deviation immediately. The pulse and respiration will go up if the horse is in pain, has a fever or is frightened.

Appetite

A horse that is not eating is trying to tell you something. A horse may go off his feed due to disease, injury, metabolic dysfunction or tiredness. He may also be trying to say that the food is of poor quality or that you are over-feeding him.

Skin and coat condition

The coat should be glossy, smooth and silky. The skin should be loose and pliable, and, when picked up and released, should return smoothly and easily to its former condition (7) and (8). Poor coat and skin condition may be due to a parasite burden, a poor diet or dehydration.

Observation

Any lumps, bumps and unusual heat must be noted immediately. Inflammation is a sign of damage and must always be taken seriously.

Blood testing

Blood testing is an invaluable tool in helping the vet to diagnose illness or to assess well-being and fitness to compete. Indeed, sub-clinical illness which causes below-par performance may be identified only through blood testing. For blood tests to be of maximum use, they should be taken regularly throughout the training programme. This allows a picture of the horse's normal blood profile to be built up.

The blood is analysed by looking at the number and type of cells present (haematology) and by examining the blood serum (biochemistry). The normal range of blood-test values for a thoroughbred-type horse is given in Table 5.

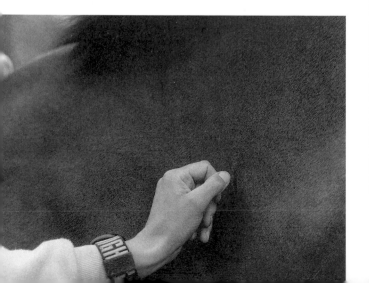

7 and **8** A pinch of skin taken on the neck or shoulder should return to normal rapidly when released

Table 5 Normal range of blood-test values	
Haematology	
Red-cell count	8·5–11 million/mm³
Haemoglobin concentration	13–17 g/100 ml (0·4–0·6 oz/0·2 pint)
Packed-cell volume	34–44 per cent
Mean corpuscular volume	38–45 Femto litre
Mean corpuscular haemoglobin concentration	32–39 g/100 ml (1·1–1·4 oz/0·2 pint)
White cells:	6–12000/mm³
neutrophils	2–8000/mm³
lymphocytes	2–4000/mm³
eosinophils	1–600/mm³
monocytes	1–600/mm³
basophils	20–50/mm³
Biochemistry	
Serum proteins:	
total	55–75 g/l (2–2·6 oz/2 pints)
albumin	25–41 g/l (0·9–1·5 oz/2 pints)
globulins	25–41 g/l(0·9–1·5 oz/2 pints) – 1:1 ratio
Urea	20–45 mg/ml
CPK	20–80 international units/l

Interpretation of the blood test is a veterinary surgeon's job, requiring experience and expertise, but the following signs can be looked for.

Bacterial infection
- increased total white-cell count
- increased percentage of neutrophils

Viral infection
- decreased total white-cell count
- more lymphocytes

Anaemia
- reduced red-cell count
- low haemoglobin concentration
- low packed-cell volume

Dehydration
- high packed-cell volume

Muscle damage
- high CPK (a muscle enzyme)

Thermography

Although the horse's legs may be carefully examined for heat and swelling, by the time these external signs become apparent the internal damage may already be extensive. In an effort to reduce this insidious injury, many trainers use technical equipment to assess a horse's fitness. Thermography uses an infra-red camera to record changes in temperature and can be used to spot wear and tear, indicating areas in which inflammatory reaction has begun but not yet led to pain/swelling (fig. 11).

This sort of equipment is expensive and specialized, but it is possible to buy hand-held thermometers which, skimmed about a centimetre (half an inch) above the leg, give a digital read-out. The best results are obtained using 'provocative cooling'. The legs are splashed with alcohol to cool them, and the thermometer measures which spot heats up most quickly.

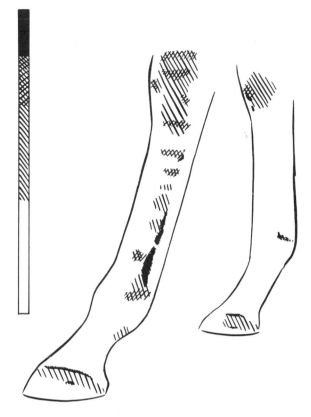

Fig. 11 The image produced by a thermography scan shows the varying temperatures in the legs, and can be used to detect inflammatory reaction

Ultrasound imaging

Ultrasound imaging uses ultrasound waves to produce a detailed scan of body tissue. Having a horse's legs 'scanned' is now, along with X-rays, an accepted part of the veterinary examination for soundness, particularly for more expensive horses. The scan will show areas of damage in the tendons and ligaments of the lower leg, and can be very useful in diagnosing tendon injury and monitoring its healing. Generally speaking the veterinary surgeon is looking for dark spots indicating fluid-filled areas caused by inflammation. Like X-rays, these scans can be difficult to interpret and require an experienced practitioner.

Force plates

The Swiss-designed Kagi gait-analysis system is designed to provide the vet and trainer with another pair of 'eyes'. The horse is walked or trotted over a rubber track which carries sensors. The sensors pick up information about the way the horse is putting his feet to the ground, by recording the forces which act on the horse's legs, independently and jointly with the other legs. The computer print-out obtained can be compared to print-outs taken from sound horses and to other print-outs obtained from that particular horse, helping the vet to diagnose lameness and the trainer to assess soundness. Again, interpretation of the results is not easy and one-off readings are of limited use.

Lactic-acid monitoring

A major goal of training is to increase the horse's tolerance to the lactic-acid build-up incurred during fast, anaerobic work. As the horse gets fitter, he can travel faster before lactic-acid production starts, and the anaerobic threshold is delayed. If the threshold stops rising it indicates that the horse has reached his limit in terms of lactic-acid tolerance, and the limit of his ability to gallop fast. If the threshold starts to fall, the horse may be ill or over-trained.

A step test can be conducted, consisting of a series of work-outs at slow, medium and fast speeds. The horse is jogged between tests to get the heart rate down to about 100 b.p.m. before he is asked to work again. The test is carried out under consistent conditions and the lactic-acid build-up of the horse is monitored: blood samples are taken before training starts and after each of the three speeds in the work-out, and analysed for lactic-acid content. A graph of lactic-acid values and the speed of the exercise can then be plotted, which will demonstrate where the anaerobic threshold lies. Training a horse just above the lactic-acid threshold helps to achieve rapid progress in the horse's ability to perform fast work over a distance, and appears to reduce the incidence of training and racing injuries.

Heart-rate monitors

The horse's heart rate can be recorded instantaneously for use by rider or driver with a heart-rate monitor. Electrodes pressed against the horse's skin pick up the electrical activity of the heart as it beats, and this information is transferred to a digital-read-out display attached to the rider's wrist or thigh so that the heart rate can be monitored at any time during exercise (fig. 12). Some models store this information for future analysis.

One of the aims of interval training is to make the horse work anaerobically for short periods, and without a heart-rate

Fig. 12 A heart-rate monitor, showing (on the right) the digital read-out display, and (on the left) the electrodes which are placed underneath the saddle and girth

monitor this is accomplished by taking the horse's pulse after one minute of walking recovery. If the heart rate is between 120 and 150 b.p.m., beneficial stress has occurred. A heart-rate monitor takes all the guesswork out of training, as the horse can be worked to his heart rate, not to a speed or distance, allowing controlled stress of the body systems. As the horse gets fitter, the heart rate for a given piece of work falls, and the horse can be asked to work faster or for longer periods. It may actually be quite hard to get a horse to work anaerobically when he is near peak fitness, but the heart-rate monitor will tell you how fast the horse needs to go to accomplish this.

The horse's resting heart rate lies between 36 and 42 beats per minute. Exercise and stress such as pain, illness or excitement will cause the heart rate to increase. At walk the heart rate might be expected to be about 60 beats per minute, at trot about 80 beats per minute and a fit horse might canter with a heart rate around 110 beats per minute. A horse that spooks or shies, even in walk, may rocket the heart rate up into the hundreds but this should soon fall as the horse calms down. As the speed of the canter or the steepness of the terrain increases so the heart rate will rise so that the sprinting horse may record heart rates of up to 240 per minute.

The fitter the horse the faster he will go for a certain heart rate, thus if a horse is trained by heart rate rather than speed, as the horse gets fitter the speed of the work will increase but the heart rate will not. Standardized exercise tests in equine research programmes often use heart rate monitors so that horses can be worked at predetermined heart rates – in simple terms the horses that go faster at the set heart rate are fitter and are responding to the diet or exercise programme that is the subject of the research.

HOW TO DECIDE WHETHER YOUR HORSE IS FIT TO RUN

- With any fitness programme, regardless of the discipline for which you are training the horse, there should be a point at which you know the horse is fit enough to compete. In many cases, the rider can tell by the way the horse 'feels' that he is fit to compete, but this 'feel' make take years to acquire, so how does the newcomer to the sport cope?
- Your training programme must be designed to include examples of the type of stress the horse will experience in competition. For example, the Novice event horse has to gallop at 520 m.p.m., so the optimum time for the cross-country is between four-and-a-half and five minutes. The final fast-work test will include these elements: five-minute slow canters, including short bursts of faster work. In this way, the horse is exposed to the type of stress to which he will be subjected in competition, without actually working as hard as he will in competition.
- If the horse can recover from the following canter work-out in ten minutes, he is fit enough to compete.

Canter 1: five minutes at 400 m.p.m.
walk three minutes
Canter 2: four minutes at 400 m.p.m.
one minute at 500 m.p.m.
walk three minutes
Canter 3: four minutes at 400 m.p.m.
one minute at 500 m.p.m., building up to 550 m.p.m.

- A similar type of exercise test may be built into any programme.

3

FEEDING THE COMPETITION HORSE

An essential ingredient of any training programme is correct feeding. No matter how well-trained the horse, without good nutrition he will not be able to perform at his best. Feeding must ensure that the horse's demand for vital nutrients is met by a balanced, palatable ration.

The horse's digestive system

The digestive tract of the horse is an open-ended tube, which begins at the mouth and ends at the anus (figs. 13 and 14). As food passes through the 'tube', it is broken down, both physically and chemically, into its constituent nutrients. These are then absorbed through the gut wall and enter the bloodstream for further processing in the horse's body.

The 'tube' consists of different parts which vary in function, length and diameter. The major regions are the mouth, stomach, small intestine, large intestine (caecum, large colon and small colon) and rectum. This layout is exactly the same as a dog or a human, yet there are important differences which allow the horse to survive on forage – a human would not look too healthy on a diet of grass!

Table 6 Lengths of parts of the horse's intestine

Area	Relative length %	Actual length metres (feet)	Relative capacity %	Actual capacity litres (gallons)
Stomach	–	–	8·5	18 (3–5)
Small intestine	75	22 (70–90)	30	64 (12–16)
Caecum	4	1 (2–3)	16	34 (7–8)
Large colon	11	3·5 (10–14)	38·5	81 (18–20)
Small colon and rectum	10	3 (9)	7	15 (2–3)
Total	100	29·5 (97)	100	212 (47)

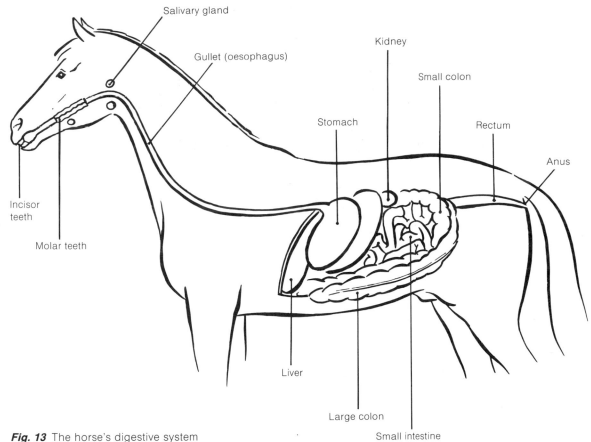

Fig. 13 The horse's digestive system

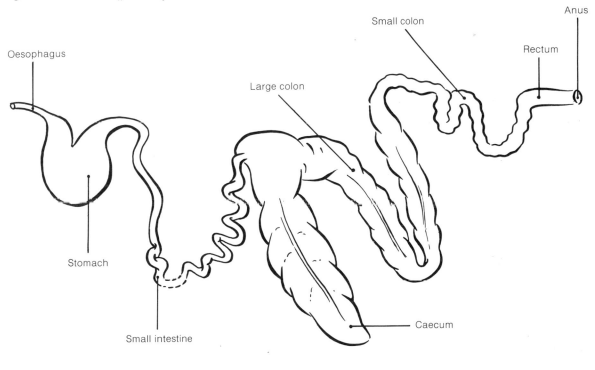

Fig. 14 The layout of the horse's gut

The mouth

The horse's head is a vehicle for a great battery of grinding teeth called molars, which are designed to break food down mechanically before it passes into the gut.

The lips   The upper lip is strong, mobile and sensitive, and the horse uses it to sort through the feed on offer, before manoeuvring the food between its teeth. The incisors or biting teeth can bite off pieces of food in a selective fashion, and, if necessary, can graze a pasture very closely.

The tongue   The tongue then moves the food to the molar teeth, which pulverize the food into smaller pieces suitably lubricated by saliva for swallowing.

The teeth   The horse has three types of tooth (**fig. 15**):

- incisors or biting teeth in the front of the mouth
- tushes or canine teeth
- molars or grinding teeth lining each side of the jaw bone (the cheek teeth)

There are six incisors in each jaw: two corner, two lateral and two central incisors, which are used to age the horse. There are twelve molars to each jaw, six on each side. Adult male horses (and some mares) have two tushes in each jaw, between the incisors and molars, so mares have a total of thirty-six teeth and geldings and stallions have forty teeth.

The horse's head is shaped so that the upper jaw is wider than the lower one (**fig. 16**). The molars overlap each other at the sides, allowing a sideways movement of the jaw that shears the food. As the jaw moves from side to side during chewing, the molars grind against each other, but the lower ones do not reach the outer edge of the upper molars, and the upper ones

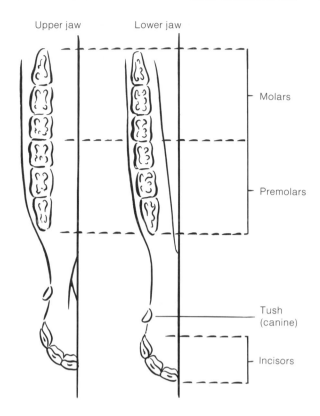

Fig. 15 The horse's teeth

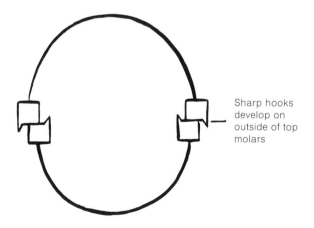

Fig. 16 There is an incomplete overlap of the upper and lower jaw

never reach the inner edge of the lower molars. The more refined the shape of the horse's head, the more exaggerated this will be, resulting in sharp edges on the outside of the top molars and on the inner edges of the bottom molars. These can cut the tongue and cheeks, making eating painful. Quidding or dropping half-chewed food from the mouth is a sign of sharp molar teeth. The vet or horse dentist can rasp or float these sharp edges – a horse's teeth should be checked twice a year and rasped if necessary.

After sufficient chewing, the horse swallows a bolus of food which passes down the gullet or oesophagus to the stomach. The oesophagus is a narrow muscular tube which can become blocked, leading to choke.

The stomach

The stomach is relatively small compared to the size of the horse and the rest of the gut – hence the 'rule of good feeding' that everybody remembers best: 'feed little and often'. The empty stomach of a 16 h.h. horse is about the size of a rugby ball and can stretch to accommodate about 18 litres (3–5 gallons). The shape of the stomach means that it is never more than two-thirds full (fig. 17), so it will hold about 9–13 litres (2–3 gallons) – about two-thirds of a standard water bucket. A 4 lb (1·8 kg) feed, or one that fills two-thirds of

a stable bucket, is adequate; bigger feeds are wasteful. Feed more frequently if you want the horse to have more feed.

A full stomach will also put pressure on the diaphragm (the muscular sheet which separates the lungs and the guts) preventing the horse from filling his lungs effectively – hence the rule 'do not work fast for at least one hour after feeding'. Nobody wants to go for a cross-country run straight after Sunday lunch! Exercise also causes the hormone adrenalin to be released; blood is diverted from the gut to the muscles and digestion is inhibited.

The shape of the horse's stomach means that, when he drinks, the water tends to wash over the top of any food present in the stomach. Water also passes through the stomach wall rapidly. It is more useful to ensure that the horse has a constant supply of fresh, clean water than it is to water before feeding.

The small intestine

From the stomach the food passes to the small intestine, a narrow muscular tube housing many glands. Here, chemicals called enzymes act on the food to break it down to its constituent nutrients. The resulting fats, amino acids, simple carbo-hydrates, minerals and vitamins are absorbed across the gut wall into the horse's body. At this stage, the remaining food consists of the roughage part of the diet and waste or indigestible products, with the easily digested, soluble part of the food having been digested in the small intestine. Food then passes to the large intestine.

The large intestine

So far the process of digestion in the horse seems little different to that in the human. The horse can, however, thrive on a diet of grass, while we would look decidedly ill!

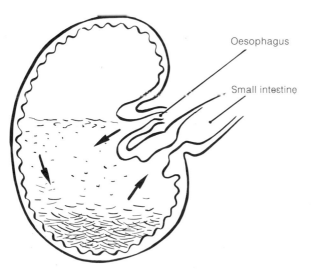

Oesophagus

Small intestine

Fig. 17 A side view of the opened stomach

So what makes the horse different? The answer lies in the horse's hind gut or large intestine, which is able to extract the energy locked up in the tough, fibrous part of plants. The large intestine consists of four parts: the caecum, the large colon, the small colon and the rectum, and is only held in place in the abdomen by its bulk. If the gut is too empty problems may arise, so you must feed plenty of roughage.

The large intestine contains bacteria which break down the fibrous part of the diet. The results of the bacterial breakdown of fibre are absorbed by the horse and used to produce energy. The bacteria can also synthesize many vitamins.

There are millions of bacteria present in the caecum and large colon. They do not take kindly to sudden changes in their environment, which may be caused by rapid changes in the horse's diet, and this can lead to severe disruptions. These disruptions are manifested as diarrhoea, laminitis, colic or plain bad temper, and once an imbalance in the microbial population has occurred it can take months to return to normal. Bacteria can, however, adapt to slow changes in the diet, so make any dietary changes gradually.

The vital nutrients

In order to design a balanced ration, it is necessary to understand what nutrients the horse requires. The six necessary ingredients of the horse's diet are water, carbohydrates, fats, proteins, minerals and vitamins.

Water

Water is essential in the horse's diet; foals contain 75–80 per cent water and older horses contain about 50 per cent water. Horses will die relatively quickly if deprived of water, and it is obviously vital that the water level is maintained. A stabled horse will normally drink 20–40 litres (5–10 gallons), depending on how much work he is doing and the climatic conditions. The performance horse should not be deprived of water for more than thirty minutes before exercise – he is unlikely to gorge himself with water if he has free access to it. It is better not to allow the horse free access to water after heavy exercise, but to give little and often until respiratory rates are back to normal.

Carbohydrates

Carbohydrates can be put into two groups: *simple carbohydrates*, including starch, glycogen and sugars; and *complex carbohydrates*, including cellulose and lignin.

Simple carbohydrates Starch and sugars are found in plants and grains – starch is the plant's form of stored carbohydrate. Simple carbohydrates are mainly digested in the small intestine of the horse; they are broken down, absorbed into the bloodstream and transported to the liver, mainly in the form of sugars. Glucose, a simple sugar, is the ultimate source of energy for most cells in the horse's body. Glucose is stored as glycogen, but the amount of glycogen that can be stored is limited, so excess glucose is converted to fat and stored in fat or adipose tissue.

Young plants, such as grasses, contain large amounts of sugars and simple carbohydrates, whereas grains, such as oats, barley and maize, contain high levels of starch. When large quantities of spring grass and cereals are eaten by the horse, high levels of glucose enter the bloodstream.

Complex carbohydrates Cellulose is found in all plant-cell walls. The horse does not have digestive enzymes capable of breaking down these walls to release the valuable carbohydrate contained within them, but the bacteria and micro-organisms living in the horse's caecum and large intestine can break down and digest cellulose. Cellulose is broken down by the bacteria, absorbed into the horse's bloodstream, taken to the liver and converted to glucose. This is why a horse can survive on a diet of grass, while we would look rather thin and hungry! Cellulose is the fibrous part of the horse's diet, found in grass, hay, silage etc., and this fibre is vital for the normal and healthy function of the horse's gut.

Lignin is another complex carbohydrate found in stemmy materials. This cannot be broken down in the gut by the horse or its resident bacterial population; it is indigestible and is excreted in the faeces.

Measuring the energy in food Carbo-hydrates, either in the form of cereals or roughage, form the largest part of the horse's diet. They provide the horse with energy, and are therefore a very important part of the competition horse's diet.

Most of us at some time have squeezed into a pair of jeans and thought, 'Oh dear, time to go on a diet!'. The correct way to diet is to design a balanced ration of a limited number of calories – in other words, one which gives you a limited energy intake. Look at your yoghurt pot – it gives you the energy value of the yoghurt, both in calories *and* joules (a joule is the metric equivalent of a calorie). The energy value of horse feeds is measured in megajoules (MJ). Oats contain about 14 MJ of digestible energy (D.E.) per kg (6·4 MJ/lb), whereas horse and pony cubes (pellets) may only contain 10 MJDE per kg (4·5 MJ/lb). You would have to feed 1·5 kg (3·3 lb) of cubes to supply with the same energy as 1 kg (2·2 lb) of oats; conversely 0·7 kg (1·5 lb) of oats would replace 1 kg (2·2 lb) of cubes.

The energy requirement of your horse will depend on many factors, but principally his size and the amount of work he is doing. Once these are known, it is fairly simple to work out his energy requirements in terms of megajoules per day, and therefore how much feed he must get. Think back to your diet book – you are given a table and, depending on your height, build and lifestyle, you are allocated a certain number of calories a day.

Fats

Horse diets contain about four per cent fat, and it is a relatively minor source of energy compared to carbohydrate. Fat is, however, a useful fuel store. It also acts as a protective layer under the skin and around the internal organs, and is essential for good skin and coat condition.

Fats contain 2·25 times more energy than carbohydrates, but there are limitations in their conversion to energy and horses have to be 'trained' to utilize more of them. Carbohydrates are still the main energy source for horses.

Proteins

Protein makes up the majority of body tissue in forms as diverse as muscle, hair and hoof. Protein is needed in the diet for body building and tissue repair, so the highest percentage of protein is required in the diet of young, growing horses. This requirement declines gradually as the horse reaches maturity, when only enough protein to replace worn-out body tissue is needed.

Proteins are made up of simple building blocks called amino acids. More than twenty amino acids occur naturally, and the horse can make some of these – known as non-essential amino acids – in the body. Some cannot be made in the body and must be supplied in the diet: there are eleven of these essential amino acids, the most important being lysine, methionine and tryptophan. Some proteins will contain higher levels of the essential amino acids than others: these are high-quality proteins and are important when feeding the growing horse. The amino acid most likely to be deficient in the horse's diet is lysine. A deficiency will severely affect protein synthesis in the horse's body, and poor growth will result. All cereals are low in lysine.

Except during starvation, proteins are of little importance as an energy source, and, contrary to many horse owners' belief, working adult horses do not require a high protein ration. Look after the energy, and the protein will look after itself.

Measuring the protein in food Foods can be chemically analysed to give the crude protein percentage, which is the value you see written on bags of compound feeds. This value is only a guideline, as it gives you no idea how digestible that protein is, nor any guide to protein quality. Bran, for instance, has a high crude-protein value, but low digestibility and a poor balance of amino acids.

Minerals and vitamins

The competition horse is usually stabled with limited access to grass and fed a variety of conserved, processed and heat-treated feeds. The mineral and vitamin levels of the feeds will have suffered by these treatments, and the horse's ability to synthesize water-soluble vitamins in the gut will be upset by rapid dietary changes and stress. Consequently, a horse needs a mineral and vitamin supplement if a traditional hay, oats and bran diet is being fed.

If a good-quality compound foodstuff is used, as specified by the manufacturer, a supplement may not be necessary, but all competition horses should have access to salt. A salt lick in the manger is usually adequate, but if the horse will not lick this, a level dessertspoon (10 ml) of salt should be added to the evening feed.

Electrolytes or electro-salts

During work the horse's muscles produce heat, which must be lost from the body to prevent heatstroke. The most efficient heat-loss mechanism is sweating. Sweating involves the evaporation of fluid, containing salts, from the surface of the horse's skin, taking with it excess heat. The horse may lose ten to twelve litres (two gallons) of sweat an hour in prolonged exercise. If forced to carry on working, the horse will become dehydrated, exhausted and unable to continue.

The electrolytes lost in horse sweat are principally sodium and chloride, with lesser amounts of potassium, calcium and magnesium. Supplements of electrolytes are designed to replenish these losses partially and to help the horse to recover from his exertions more swiftly.

Beware of over-using electrolytes, as their unnecessary feeding can actually dehydrate the horse. Only use them on the day of competition and follow the manufacturer's guidelines. If your horse has been dehydrated, your veterinary surgeon will advise whether you need to continue using electrolytes until the horse has recovered.

It is advisable to always have a salt lick in the horse's manger so that he can satisfy any need he may feel for salt. If the horse over uses the salt lick it is better to add a dessertspoon of salt to the evening feed.

What to feed the horse

In order to make a decision about what to feed the horse, the owner has to take many factors into consideration, for example:

- cost
- availability
- the horse's nutrient requirements
- quality
- the nutrient content of the feed

Feeds can be divided into two categories: concentrates and forage. Concentrates are energy feeds, and traditionally cereals have been the principal source of energy for horses in hard work. Cereal grains contain 12–16 MJDE/kg (5·5–7·3 MJ/lb) of dry matter compared to about 8·5 MJ/kg (3·9 MJ/lb) in average grass hay. In other words, 1 kg (2·2 lb) of cereals can replace up to 2 kg (4·4 lb) of hay in the ration – hence the name concentrate. As we demand a higher energy output from the horse, we have to feed him more concentrated energy sources in order to keep the ration within his appetite. This also reduces his natural grass belly.

Cereals also contain proteins, but these are less nutritionally valuable than animal protein and oil-seed protein as they are relatively deficient in the essential amino acids lysine and methionine. All cereal grains are very low in calcium, containing less than 1·5 g/kg (0·02 oz/lb) but they contain three to five times as much phosphorus. The phosphorus is principally in the form of phytate salts which reduce the availability of calcium and zinc, further increasing the horse's need for a calcium supplement.

Calcium can be provided by feeding either limestone flour or dicalcium phosphate. Limestone flour consists of calcium carbonate and should be fed at a rate of about 25g per day. Dicalcium phosphate also contains phosphorus, one phosphorus for every two calcium, this helps ensure that the correct calcium to phosphorus ratio (of around 1.5:1) is maintained. This should be fed at a rate of about 50g per day. Growing horses and lactating and pregnant mares have higher requirements of both calcium and phosphorus.

Table 7 Nutrient values of commonly-fed concentrate feeds

	Crude protein %	Oil %	M.A.D. (modified acid detergent) Fibre g/kg (oz/lb)	Ca g/kg (oz/lb)	P g/kg (oz/lb)	Lysine %	D.E. MJ/kg (MJ/lb)
Oats	9·6	4·5	17 (?)	0·7 (?)	3·0 (?)	3·2	11–12 (5–5·5)
Naked oats	13·5	9·7	3·2 (?)	0·2 (?)	0·4 (?)	5	16 (7·3)
Barley	9·5	1·8	7 (?)	0·6 (?)	3·3 (?)	3·1	13 (6)
Maize	8·5	3·8	3 (?)	0·2 (?)	3·0 (?)	2·6	14 (6·4)
Linseed	22	32	7·6 (?)	2·4 (?)	5·2 (?)	7·7	18·5 (8·4)
Extracted soyabean meal	44	1	10 (?)	2·4 (?)	6·3 (?)	26	13·3 (6)
Wheatbran	15·5	3	12 (?)	1 (?)	12 (?)	6	11 (5)
Sugarbeet pulp	7	1	34 (?)	10 (?)	11 (?)	2·8	10·5 (4·8)

The 'heating' effect of grain

Grain is often said to be 'heating', meaning that it results in a horse being over-excited and difficult to control. This heating effect stems from two sources.

1. Over-feeding energy – many 'hot' horses are simply getting too much energy for the job that they are doing, and a reduction in the concentrate ration and an increase in the roughage will solve many problems. Behavioural problems are made worse by confining the horse to his stable for twenty-three hours a day and then working him to increase his fitness – a veritable timebomb!
2. Fermentation – any grain passing through into the large intestine is rapidly fermented by the intestinal micro-organisms. This increases the acidity of the caecum, which may lead to discomfort, and the products of digestion pass very quickly into the bloodstream. There is then a rise in blood levels of glucose and V.F.A.s, which stimulates the metabolic rate, thus 'heating' the horse both literally and mentally. Processing cereals increases the amount of digestion in the small intestine, reduces caecal fermentation and keeps the metabolism more stable.

Compound feeds

Compound feeds are convenience feeds for horses and have several advantages:

- convenience
- standardized diets for specific purposes
- constant quality
- good shelf life
- freedom from dust
- palatability
- uniform weight and size, making the feeding routine more convenient
- economy of labour, transportation and storage
- no wastage

There are, however, some disadvantages to compound feeds:

- one cannot tell good-quality from poor-quality ingredients
- the horse may find them boring to eat

The first disadvantage can be overcome by always using products from reputable compounders and seeking advice from their nutritionists. The label on the bag has to declare certain ingredients by law, and this can be a useful reference; some manufacturers now include digestible energy and digestible crude protein, which is very useful. Remember that, although straight feeds such as oats may *look* the same, you cannot see the protein and energy in them any more than you can in a cube (pellet). The bag that a cube comes from states its feed value, but a bag of oats does not have to do so. Oats can vary in their protein content by up to eight per cent from one season to the next or one farm to the next, and in order to meet the legally declared analysis, the manufacturer must analyse the oats and then add a suitable protein supplement to balance the compound.

Feeding compounds If we are honest, few of us feed compounds as intended – we add oats or barley to them, believing that horses find them 'boring'. We must be careful, however, not to make our horses fussy, and why should cubes, properly fed, be any more boring than grass? To combat boredom, coarse mixes (sweet feeds) have been produced – muesli for horses! We think that they look nice and are good enough to eat, and we can also see what is in them, which is enough to induce us to pay extra for them. We still continue to add grain to the mix, however, which unbalances the compound and defeats one of the reasons for feeding a compound – a convenient, balanced ration in one bag. If you feel that your horse needs more energy than the present cube is giving him, then buy a higher-energy performance mix – there are plenty of these available.

If you are in any doubt, ring the manufacturer and ask for help. Any reputable company will have a technical adviser who should be able to answer your questions.

A balanced ration provides everything necessary to enable the horse to do the work demanded. Compound feeds, fed with hay, haylage or grazing, are designed to provide a balanced ration. Other feeds such as oats and bran can be mixed with cubes, however adding large amounts can upset the energy and protein balance. Compound feeds are mixtures of nutritionally balanced ingredients; instead of mixing oats, bran and other feeds at home, the manufacturer does it for you. Compound feeds also contain the minerals and vitamins frequently lacking in a traditional ration of hay and oats. Cubes and coarse mixes have the advantage of meeting the requirements of all horses, allowing you to feed a consistent, convenient and correctly balanced diet.

Ingredients commonly used in compound feeds include:

- micronised barley – a cooked form of barley providing energy
- soya bean meal – an excellent source of high quality protein
- oats – the traditional grain fed to horses providing energy for work
- maize – steamed and flaked, and therefore easily digestible for the horse. The high energy content means that it is good for condition
- micronised peas and beans – a source of energy and protein, traditionally fed to outwintered horses to help keep condition
- locust beans – a palatable and sweet tasting ingredient of some coarse mixes
- linseed cake – a source of protein and B vitamins. Traditionally fed boiled to help coat condition
- lucerne nuts – a palatable and high quality source of fibre and protein
- concentrate pellets – most mixes will contain a small cube with minerals and vitamins to balance the ration
- oat fed pellet – an oat by-product and a source of the fibre needed in 'non-heating' diets

Table 8 Typical nutrient values of compound feeds

	Crude Oil %	Crude fibre %	Crude protein %	Total lysine %	Digestible energy MJ/kg(MJ/lb)	Total ash %
Horse and pony cubes (pellets)	3	14–15	10	0·45	9 (4·1)	9–10
Performance cubes (pellets)	3·5–4	8·5	12–13	0·55	12 (5·5)	8–10
Stud cubes (pellets)	3	9–10	13–15	0·65	11 (5)	8–10
Creep feed	4–4·5	6·5–7·5	17–18	0·9	13 (6)	7–9
Yearling cubes (pellets)	3–3·5	8·5	15–16	0·75	11 (5)	7–9

Rationing

The ration of a performance horse is decided after three important factors have been assessed:

- size
- condition
- work done

Size

The amount of food that a horse needs to keep him alive and to maintain his body weight is called the maintenance ration. It is determined by his weight; common sense tells us that a big horse eats more than a little one! Horses will eat about 2·5 per cent of their body weight per day, so a 500 kg (1100 lb) horse (a 16 hh middle-weight) will eat 12·5 kg (28 lb) of food a day. Table 9 illustrates approximate body weights and appetites for different horses and ponies.

Condition

One of the first things anybody notices about a horse, regardless of size or type, is his condition – is he fat or thin? If he is thin, the nutrient requirement for energy will be higher to enable him to put on condition. Assessment of condition is very subjective and care must be taken to look at the whole picture, as, while a show horse would look fat in a racing yard, a racehorse would look very lean in a show-ing yard. The type and intensity of work that the horse is doing must also be taken into consideration.

Work done

One of the old-established rules of feeding is to feed the horse for the amount and intensity of the work that he is doing. It is important for the horse's health, your safety and your joint success not to over- or under-feed your horse for his degree of fitness. This means that one of the first steps in rationing is to establish the horse's performance or competitive goal in order to get the horse to the correct level of fitness and feeding. There is no point in having a horse – particularly a youngster or a child's pony – too fit and over-fed for the task in hand.

Light work would include daily hacking or light schooling with the occasional competition at weekends. Medium work would be hunting one day a week or one day horse trials. Hard work would be hunting two days a week or three day eventing while fast work is racing.

Height hands	Girth cm (ins)	Body weight kg (lb)	Appetite kg (lb) dry matter
11	135–145 (53–57)	200–260 (440–570)	4·5–6 (10–13)
12	140–150 (55–59)	230–290 (500–640)	5–7 (11–15·5)
13	150–160 (59–63)	290–350 (640–770)	6·5–8 (14–17·5)
14	160–170 (63–67)	350–420 (770–920)	8–9·5 (17·5–21)
15	170–185 (67–73)	420–520 (920–1140)	10–12·5 (22–27·5)
16	185–195 (73–77)	500–600 (1100–1320)	12–14 (26·5–31)
17	195–210 (77–83)	600–725 (1320–1600)	13–18 (29–40)

Table 9 The relationship between height, girth, body weight and appetite

Note: the values in this table are averages and only approximate.

The ratio of forage to concentrates

In the practical situation when a new horse arrives in the yard, you have to decide what to put on the feedboard immediately – there is no time to get out your calculator! A 'rule of thumb' used for many years as a guideline to horses' rations is a simple table, relating the intensity of the horse's work to the ratio of forage to concentrates fed, as shown in Table 10.

Table 10 Ratios of forage to concentrates		
Work level	Hay	Concentrates
Resting	100	0
Light	75	25
Medium	60	40
Hard	40	60
Fast	30	70

On this basis, a 500 kg (1100 lb) horse in hard work is fed 40 per cent concentrates and 60 per cent forage, resulting in a ration of 5 kg (11 lb) of concentrates and 7·5 kg (16·5 lb) of hay. It is best to feed a horse slightly below his appetite, so that he is always eager for his next concentrate feed and has always finished his haynet when you come to fill it again. Beware of the *ad lib* feeding system – often the hay rack is constantly topped up so that the hay at the bottom becomes mouldy, and the horse becomes over-fussy and wasteful. If you feed a weighed ration of hay and concentrates, within the horse's appetite, he should always eat it up. If he does not eat all his hay and concentrates, it may indicate that the quality of the feed is not up to scratch or that the horse is off-colour.

GENERAL GUIDELINES

- All horses are individuals and must be treated as such. Once a ration has been calculated and is being fed, the horse must be monitored to ensure that the ration is suitable.
- A supply of fresh, clean water must be available to the horse at all times.
- The foods must be of good quality and acceptable to the horse – is he enjoying his food?
- Not only must the foods satisfy the horse's nutritional requirements, he must also be psychologically satisfied, not bored and craving for roughage.
- The horse's condition must be checked by eye, tape or weighbridge. The horse may be gaining or losing weight. Is this what is wanted? If not, alter the ration accordingly. Horses have an optimum performance weight and should be kept to it as closely as possible.
- The horse's temperament and behaviour may affect the ration that is fed. Part-bred horses may need more concentrates and less bulk, as they are better doers and (usually) more placid. Routine and a quiet yard may save feed, as horses will not be fretting in their boxes.
- The horse's environment must be monitored. In a cold spell, more food and an extra blanket may be needed. A clipped horse may need more food to maintain his condition if he is not adequately rugged up. In hot weather, horses may go off their concentrate ration because their maintenance requirement has fallen; do not worry about this unless they start to lose condition.
- Horses must be wormed regularly and have their teeth checked for sharp edges.
- Some horses are poor doers, perhaps due to a gut damaged by worms early in life, and will always need extra attention given to their feeding.

Practical feeding

Eventing

The event horse has to be fit enough to gallop and jump at speed, and yet disciplined enough to perform dressage and show jumping. This has led to many event riders trying to keep their horses mentally and physically happy by feeding as few concentrates as possible and turning their horses out in the field every day. The three-day-event horse may have a very rigorous training programme, and yet only compete in a few events on the run up to the main competition before being turned away, while the lower-level horse may compete once a week throughout the long event season. These horses have widely differing feed requirements.

Many riders worry that their horse is not eating enough during a two- or three-day event, but, as long as the horse is eating his hay and drinking normally, there is no need to worry unduly. The horse has enough energy stored in his liver and muscles to see him through three days of competition. Prior to the event, do not be tempted to change the horse's ration. Some people reduce or cut out the sugar-beet pulp before the event, while others would only reduce or omit the beet pulp on the morning of cross-country day. If the horse frets away from home, reduce the quantity of concentrate food and use high-energy, palatable ingredients such as milk pellets and flaked maize. Generally speaking, it is better not to fiddle with the horse's feed too much, as you may just cause problems.

A three-day-event horse should have a concentrate feed no less than four hours before the start time of Phase A. If he is competing in the afternoon, he could also have a small haynet (**fig. 18**). If the horse has had free access to fresh water, there is no reason why he should have his water bucket taken away before he competes – why should he suddenly decide to have a huge drink?

A Novice event horse could munch on a haynet while being plaited on the morning of his competition, but if he has early times he should not receive any bulk while travelling until after his cross-country. If

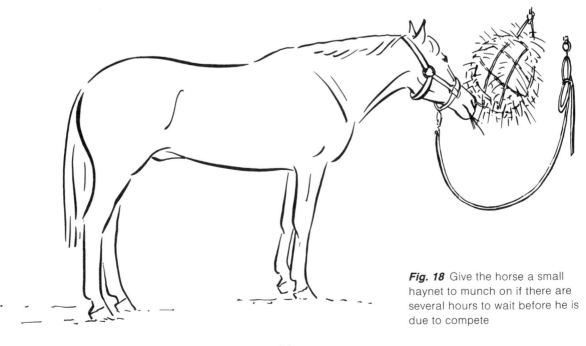

Fig. 18 Give the horse a small haynet to munch on if there are several hours to wait before he is due to compete

his cross-country time is late, he could have a small haynet while travelling. Depending on your times, he may be able to have a concentrate feed between the dressage and the show jumping, provided that there are at least two hours' digestion time. He should be offered water frequently throughout the day, and be allowed to wash his mouth out between the show jumping and the cross country, even if they are very close together.

The fluid and electrolyte balance is very important, and the horse must be watched for signs of dehydration. If a pinch of skin on the neck or shoulder lingers after it has been released and the horse has a gaunt, tucked-up appearance, he may well be dehydrated. This really can limit the next day's performance severely, so ensure that the horse drinks and provide electrolytes in the food or water.

Colic can be a problem after severe exertion, and the intestines must be kept moving. Once the horse is cool and his thirst has been quenched, he may appreciate a small bran mash, with his normal feed later on. Tired horses are easily overfaced by a large feed, but dividing the normal feed in two and feeding it at intervals may overcome this.

Endurance and long-distance riding

A horse competing in long-distance rides has to learn to make effective use of body-fat reserves as a source of energy and as a way of conserving his precious limited glucose reserves. Once all the glucose stores have been used up, the horse will become fatigued. Horses fed corn oil have been shown to digest it very efficiently, and high levels of dietary fat slow down the drop in blood glucose during endurance work. It would seem that providing a high-fat diet, containing 8 to 12 per cent total fat, may stimulate the body to use it as an energy source, thus conserving glucose and allowing the horse to work for longer before he becomes fatigued.

In practical terms, providing 8–12 per cent fat in the diet means feeding 1–1·5 litres (2–3 pints) of oil a day. This is a very high level, and, although I have successfully fed half a litre (one pint) a day, more work needs to be done before this can be recommended. Half a litre of oil is equivalent in energy terms to feeding 18 M.J.D.E per day, and means that you can drop your concentrate ration by 1·5 kg (3·5 lb) of oats per day. This is useful if you have a horse which loses condition easily or tends to become very excitable on a high-concentrate diet. Unlike cereals, where starch may pass to the large intestine to be fermented by the bacteria as outlined on page 48, oil is digested in the small intestine, so substituting oil for some of the cereal part of a ration may make the horse less 'hot'.

The provision of water for endurance horses is vital, and they should be accustomed to drinking during the ride whenever possible, as giving water little and often prevents dehydration without causing problems. Electrolytes are very important to endurance horses. They can be given in a horse's feed for a day or two prior to the ride, and during the ride in water or sugar-beet liquid. They are sometimes given by syringing concentrated electrolyte solution into the horse's mouth during a ride, but this must never be done before the horse has started to drink well, or the strong salt solution in the horse's stomach will cause fluid to be drawn into the stomach from the tissues to dilute the solution. This will in fact cause dehydration, so remember that over-use or incorrect use of electrolytes can be harmful.

Show jumping and dressage

Show jumpers and dressage horses are both trained to perform tests of obedience and accuracy, which require considerable power at more advanced levels. They do not perform fast work or endurance work and do not need to be as lean as endurance horses or eventers, but are often strongly muscled and carry quite a lot of condition. Also in contrast to endurance horses and eventers, both dressage horses and show jumpers may compete very frequently with a long competition season. The skill in feeding these horses is to maintain their condition and to keep them mentally fresh without over- or under-feeding them. It is just as important to achieve the correct overall energy content of the diet in these horses as it is in racehorses.

THE RULES OF FEEDING

Most of the rules of feeding are common sense, but they are backed up by sound scientific and practical knowledge of the horse and his digestive system, as outlined in this chapter. The basic rules to remember are:

- feed little and often
- feed plenty of roughage
- make any changes to the diet gradually
- leave at least one hour between feeding and work
- feed only good-quality, dust-free ingredients
- provide fresh, clean water at all times
- follow an effective worming programme
- have the horse's teeth rasped at least once a year

Table 11 **Rations for a 15·2–16 hh, 500 kg (1100 lb) horse at different work levels**

Work level	Digestible energy required *MJDE/kg(lb)*	Crude protein required %	Ratio of hay to concentrates	RATION *Hay: 8 MJDE/ kg(lb)* kg (lb)	Concentrate kg (lb)	Comments
Maintenance	9 (4)	7·5	90:10	9·5 (21)	1 (2)	Horse and pony cubes (pellets) (10 MJDE/kg [4·5 MJ/lb])
Light (getting fit)	9·5 (4·3)	8	80:20	8·5 (19)	2 (4·5)	As above
Light to medium (Novice horse trials)	10 (4·5)	8·5	70:30	7·5 (16)	3·5 (8)	Event cubes (pellets) (11 MJDE/kg [5 MJ/lb])
Medium (Intermediate horse trials)	11 (5)	9	60:40	6·5 (14)	5 (11)	As above
Hard (Advanced horse trials)	12 (5·5)	9·5	40:60	5·5 (12)	6·5 (14)	Racehorse cubes (pellets) (14 MJDE/kg [6·4 MJ/lb]) or oats plus protein concentrate
Fast (racing)	13·5 (6·1)	10–11	30:70	3·5 (7·5)	8·5 (19)	As above

4
HEALTH CARE

No matter how much care is taken in designing and carrying out a training and feeding programme, problems can, and will, occur. A good trainer will spot these problems early and take the appropriate action to save the horse from any long-term, lasting damage.

Preventative medicine is the use of good stable management, combined with routine veterinary treatments, to control the development and build-up of disease.

The stable environment

The horse's respiratory system must be kept healthy if he is to perform at his best. All stabled horses face a constant challenge to their lungs from dust, mould spores, mites, viruses, bacteria, humidity and noxious gases (including ammonia), all of which are present in the stable environment. This challenge can be reduced using 'dust-extracted' bedding, paper, cardboard and shavings, and by feeding soaked hay and semi-wilted forages.

Arguably the single most important factor in reducing this respiratory challenge is to ensure that the stable is adequately ventilated. Many stables are poorly ventilated because of the widely held misconception that good ventilation leads to cold and draughty boxes where horses 'don't do well'. With the correct positioning and size of air inlets and outlets, and the use of air-baffling techniques, there is no reason why a well-ventilated box cannot provide a 'comfortable' environment.

ESSENTIALS FOR A GOOD STABLE ENVIRONMENT

- generous air movement, without draughts
- a dry atmosphere with no condensation
- a reasonably uniform temperature
- dry flooring with good drainage

Ventilation

Ventilation provides a constant supply of fresh air, removing micro-organisms, noxious gases and excess moisture. Natural ventilation relies on three forces to provide air movement:

1. stack effect – warm air rises and is replaced by cool air
2. aspiration – as wind passes over the roof, air is sucked out
3. perflation – air movement from side to side and end to end of a building

The stack effect (air warmed by the horse's body rising and creating a flow of air through the stable) is the key to natural ventilation.

Air inlets should be designed so that fresh air is evenly distributed to all parts of the stable without creating draughts, with a generous air-change rate above the horse and gentle currents at horse level. Inlets may be the top half of the stable door, hopper and louvre vents and windows. Hopper (or Sheringham) windows should open inward with side cheeks to reduce down-draughts **(fig. 19)**. The aim is to direct incoming air above the horse, with secondary currents providing ventilation at horse level.

Air outlets should be at the highest point of the stable roof. In a pitched-roof building, the air outlet should be a ridge vent. A pitch of 15° or more is recommended – a lower roof pitch will inhibit air

Fig. 19 A hopper or Sheringham window, which opens with an inward slant. All windows should be protected with wire mesh or metal grilles

Fig. 20 The interior of a loose box, which is ventilated via the door, window and roof

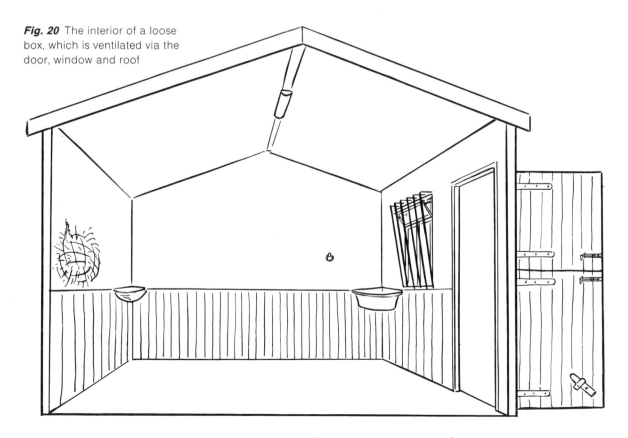

MAINTAINING A HEALTHY ENVIRONMENT

Good stable-management techniques are essential if a 'minimal-dust environment' is to be achieved. The following procedures should be carried out:

- avoid bedding up when the horse is in the stable
- do not bring a horse into a newly bedded box straight from exercise, when his respiratory system is at its most vulnerable
- remove wet bedding frequently, and avoid spillage from buckets and drinkers to reduce relative humidity and ammonia levels
- never restrict ventilation to raise the temperature of the stable; instead, put another rug on the horse or provide a heat source
- use a dust-free bedding such as shavings, paper, dust-extracted straw or one of the newer alternatives and muck out thoroughly, turning the banks regularly to prevent damp and mould building up

movement and may limit the available air capacity (fig. 20).

There has been much debate about correct ventilation rates for stables, often quoted as the number of air changes per hour, or as cubic metres per hour per kilogram of body weight. The optimum ventilation rate is determined by the horse's weight and the air volume of the stable, with the aim being to avoid stagnant air or draughts. As a general rule, a stable with a high air volume per horse will have a lower requirement for air changes and vice versa. Where horses occupy a shared air space in American barn-type stabling, a higher air change rate will be needed. If the natural ventilation is not adequate, electric fans may have to be installed. The system must meet minimum ventilation rates, avoid creating draughts and be easily manually controlled.

Vaccination

In the UK and Ireland, horses are commonly vaccinated against tetanus, influenza and rhinopneumonitis (EHV-1). All the details are recorded on a certificate (fig. 21). The principle of all vaccinations is to administer an initial course and to follow this with booster doses at regular intervals. Permanent vaccination with tetanus toxoid can be started in foals from three months of age. There is a primary vaccination of two doses separated by two to four weeks. A booster is given a year later, and then every two years thereafter. Tetanus vaccination is often combined with the influenza vaccine.

Vaccination against influenza is mandatory for horses competing under Jockey Club or F.E.I. rules, and the rules are strictly enforced. A primary course of two

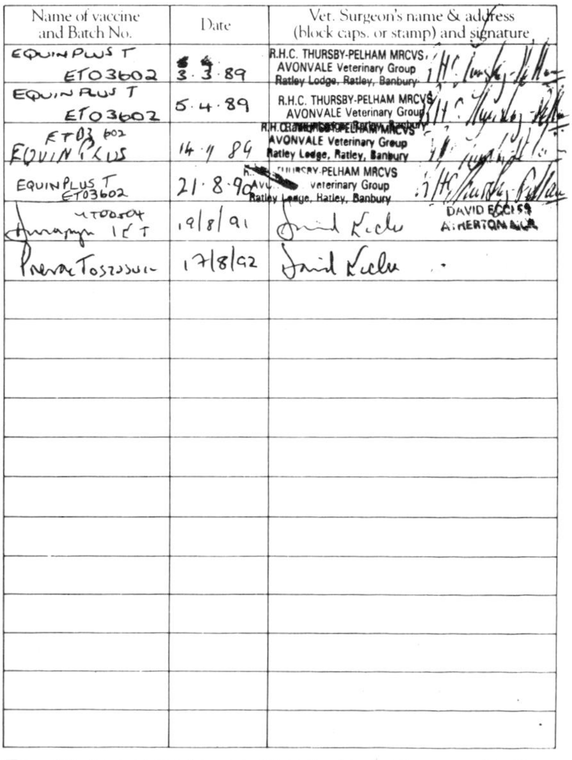

VACCINATIONS

Name of vaccine and Batch No.	Date	Vet. Surgeon's name & address (block caps. or stamp) and signature
EQUIN PLUS T ET03602	3.3.89	R.H.C. THURSBY-PELHAM MRCVS AVONVALE Veterinary Group Ratley Lodge, Ratley, Banbury
EQUIN PLUS T ET03602	5.4.89	R.H.C. THURSBY-PELHAM MRCVS AVONVALE Veterinary Group
EQUIN PLUS ET03 602	14.9 89	R.H.C. THURSBY-PELHAM MRCVS AVONVALE Veterinary Group
EQUIN PLUS T ET03602	21.8.90	R.H. THURSBY-PELHAM MRCVS AVU veterinary Group Ratley Lodge, Hatley, Banbury
ITO0404 ICT	19/8/91	David Kidner DAVID ECCLES ALHERTON MCA
Prevac Tos2usui	17/8/92	David Kidner

Fig. 21 A vaccination certificate (see also overleaf)

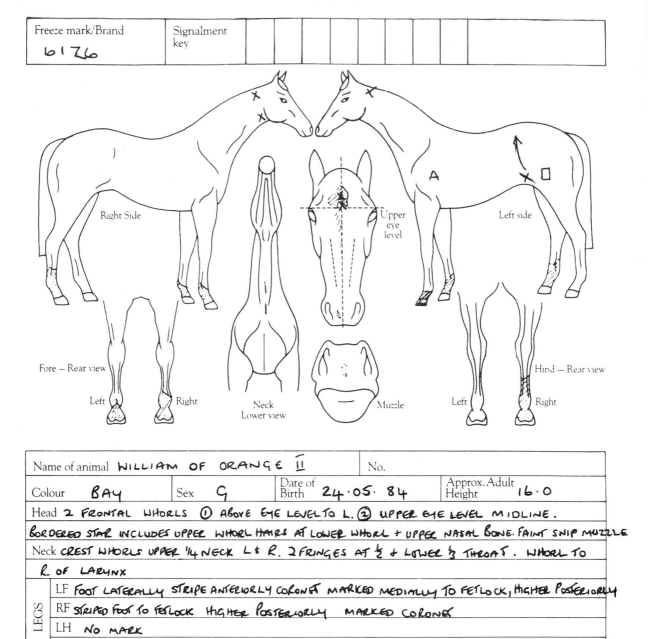

Right Side

Upper eye level

Left side

Fore — Rear view

Left Right

Neck Lower view

Muzzle

Hind — Rear view

Left Right

Name of animal **WILLIAM OF ORANGE II**   No.

Colour **BAY**	Sex **G**	Date of Birth **24.05.84**	Approx. Adult Height **16.0**

Head **2 FRONTAL WHORLS ① ABOVE EYE LEVEL TO L. ② UPPER EYE LEVEL MIDLINE.**
BORDERED STAR INCLUDES UPPER WHORL HAIRS AT LOWER WHORL + UPPER NASAL BONE. FAINT SNIP MUZZLE

Neck **CREST WHORLS UPPER ¼ NECK L & R. 2 FRINGES AT ½ & LOWER ⅓ THROAT. WHORL TO**
R OF LARYNX

LEGS
LF **FOOT LATERALLY STRIPE ANTERIORLY CORONET MARKED MEDIALLY TO FETLOCK, HIGHER POSTERIORLY**
RF **STRIPED FOOT TO FETLOCK HIGHER POSTERIORLY MARKED CORONET**
LH **NO MARK**
RH **STRIPED FOOT, CORONET MARKS. TO ½ CANNON**

Body **L. SHOULDER 'A' BRAND   L THIGH BRANDED**

V.S. Stamp and signature:
R.H.C. THURSBY-PELHAM MRCVS
AVONVALE Veterinary Group
Ratley Lodge, Ratley, Banbury

Place and Date **9.4.89. Warwickshire College**

Identification procedure: The above identification must be completed by a Veterinary Surgeon only.

The recommended procedure for identification is described in the F.E.I. booklet 'Identification of Horses'.

The diagram and written description must agree and must be sufficiently detailed to ensure the positive identification of the animal in future. White markings must be shown in red and the written description completed using **black ink in block capitals or typescript.** If there are no markings, this fact must be stated in the written description.

All head and neck whorls should be marked ("X") and described in detail. Other whorls should be similarly recorded in greys and in animals lacking sufficient other distinguishing marks. Acquired marks (" ") and other distinguishing marks, e.g. prophet's thumb mark ("Δ"), wall eye, etc., should always be noted.

Age: In the absence of documentary evidence of age, animals older than 8 years may be described as "aged".

Please leave blank: 'signalment key' top right hand box and 'No'.

injections, 21–90 days apart, is followed by a booster 150–215 days later. Boosters must then be given annually within twelve months of the last injection. This vaccine protects horses against all commonly occurring strains of equine influenza, but viruses do vary periodically and this may lead to a breakdown in immunity.

Vaccination against rhinopneumonitis is widespread in the USA. and is becoming more common in the UK. The horse has a primary vaccination course of two injections, followed by regular boosters. The immune response is short-lived, so, to be effective, boosters may have to be given every three months.

In the USA, horses also need to be vaccinated against Eastern and Western Encephalomyelitis: there is no specific treatment for this disease, making vaccination an important preventative measure. Two doses of the vaccine are given ten days apart in the early spring, with an annual booster. It is recommended that horses travelling to competitions are also protected against rabies and potomac horse fever, although opinions do vary, so it is wise to seek the advice of your veterinary surgeon.

Horses from the UK travelling abroad must have a blood sample tested for the presence of equine infectious anaemia, known as a Coggin's test. The USA and South America are high-risk areas for this disease.

Parasite control

Parasitic worms are a serious threat to horse health. There are only a few effective anthelmintic drugs, and it is important to try to preserve their effectiveness if the worm burden is to be controlled in more and more crowded paddocks. The emergence of resistant strains can be slowed down in several ways.

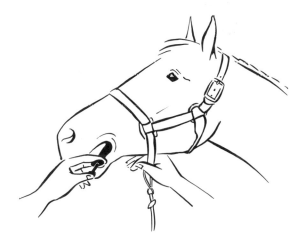

Fig. 22 Worming with paste contained in a syringe. This should be inserted far enough into the mouth to prevent the horse from spitting out the paste

It is important that all horses at an establishment are wormed correctly during the year, preferably at the same time **(fig. 22)**. Horses should be wormed every six weeks from March to October, and every eight weeks during the winter months. This is because the rate of development of infective larvae from the eggs in the dung varies during the year, taking longer during the cold winter months than during warm, wet conditions in the summer. The horse should be wormed for bots in November.

The correct drug quantity should be given to each horse, depending on his weight, which can be calculated using a weigh tape. If the horse is under-dosed, the wormer is unlikely to kill the majority of worms, while over-dosing increases the selection pressure towards resistance. The correct dose of wormer will kill about 90 per cent of worms, and not all those that survive may carry the genes for resistance (they may have survived by 'hiding' from the drug in a developmental stage, or in a fold of the intestine wall). When the next generation establishes itself, 'resistant' worms will mate with 'non-resistant' worms and the number of resistance genes will not be increased. The more you over-dose with wormer, the more 'non-resist-ant' worms will be killed, leaving only 'resistant' worms to mate and therefore increasing their resistance.

The level of pasture contamination must be kept to a minimum by reducing the number of horses in the paddocks and by removing dung on a regular basis. The number of infective worm larvae on the pasture will inevitably increase during the grazing season, but these two meas-ures will decrease the horses' total larval uptake and prevent horses being stabled during the winter with very high levels of developing parasites. There is the added danger of the development of small stron-gyle larvae being arrested. These larvae become encysted in the tissues, and can suddenly emerge in the spring, causing severe diarrhoea.

Another problem which can increase the chance of resistance developing is to buy in a horse which is harbouring a resistant strain of worms. It is wise to have a faecal worm-egg-count check carried out on the horse before purchase, and then to worm him to make sure that the drug is actually effective.

The problem of resistance means that, whatever worming programme is being used, it makes sense to alternate the wormer on an annual basis. It is very useful to carry out a faecal-worm-egg count on the dung six weeks after the first dose of the season, just before the second wormer dose. If the egg count is high, take another sample one week after the second dose to make sure that this year's principal wormer is effective.

Lameness

Problems affecting the way the horse moves are known as mechanical problems, and usually involve muscles, bone, tend-ons and ligaments.

Muscle problems

Muscle does the work that drives the horse, and part of any training programme involves developing the horse's muscles. Muscles are made up of tiny fibres lying parallel to each other, bound together by

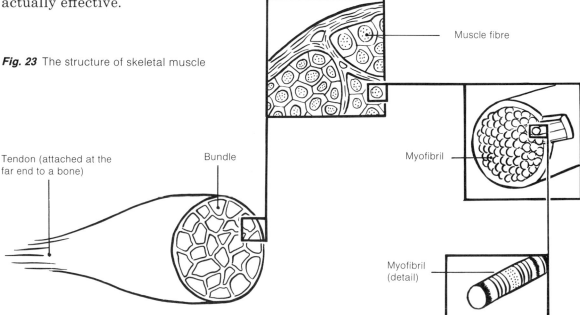

Fig. 23 The structure of skeletal muscle

Muscle fibre

Tendon (attached at the far end to a bone)

Bundle

Myofibril

Myofibril (detail)

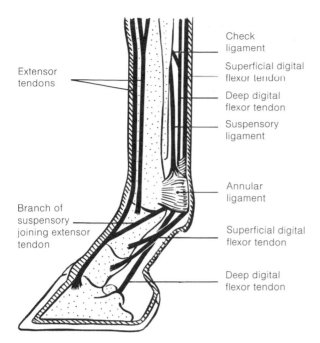

Check ligament
Superficial digital flexor tendon
Deep digital flexor tendon
Suspensory ligament
Annular ligament
Superficial digital flexor tendon
Deep digital flexor tendon

Extensor tendons

Branch of suspensory joining extensor tendon

Fig. 24 The tendons and ligaments of the lower leg

connective tissue and attached to bone via a tendon **(fig. 23)**. When the muscle contracts, it shortens and pulls on the tendon, which pulls on the bone and moves that part of the horse. The energy for contraction comes from glycogen stored in the muscle.

Muscle problems tend to arise when the muscle is tired. The lactic acid which builds up during anaerobic galloping work can damage muscle cells, and is associated with tying-up in severe cases, and with stiffness and discomfort in minor cases.

Tendon and ligament problems

Tendons and ligaments are inelastic structures; tendons connect muscle to bone, while ligaments connect bone to bone **(fig. 24)**. A tired, unbalanced horse or a horse which hits bad going when galloping may suddenly throw all his weight on a tendon, without the muscle performing its normal shock-absorbing role. The tendon

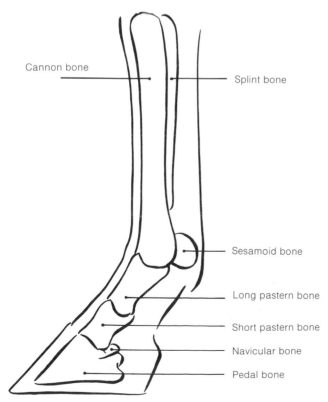

Cannon bone
Splint bone
Sesamoid bone
Long pastern bone
Short pastern bone
Navicular bone
Pedal bone

Fig. 25 The bones of the lower leg

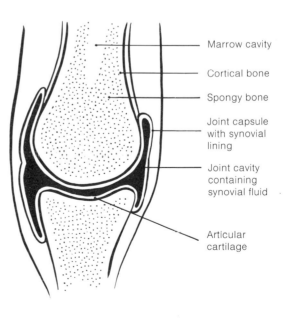

Marrow cavity
Cortical bone
Spongy bone
Joint capsule with synovial lining
Joint cavity containing synovial fluid
Articular cartilage

Fig. 26 The structure of a joint

cannot stretch, and, instead, fibres within the tendon rupture. A similar problem may occur within joints if the horse slips or twists.

Bone problems

Bones are not rigid, dead structures, but living structures that are constantly changing. The harder the horse works, the harder his bones work (see **figs. 25** and **26** on the previous page). Calcium and phosphorus are constantly moving in and out of the bone, building more bone tissue in response to work. The event horse is particularly susceptible to tiny fractures

of the stifle region, as he may drag his hind legs over a fence when he sees what lies on the other side!

All injury results in inflammation, which is in fact an essential part of healing. The signs of inflammation are:

- heat – due to increased blood supply
- pain – caused by pressure and chemicals called prostaglandins
- swelling – due to the increased blood supply leaking essential healing agents into the injured area

Heat and swelling in the horse's lower leg indicates damage and should always be taken seriously.

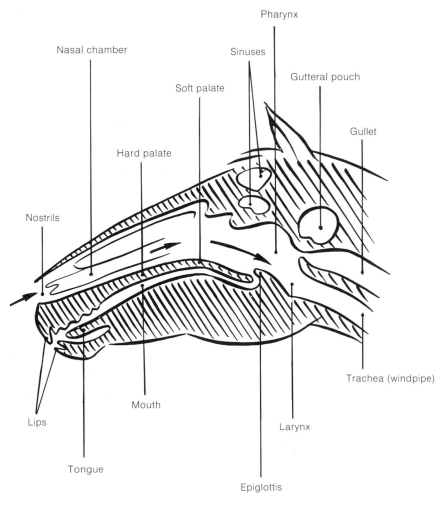

Fig. 27 The respiratory tract of the head and neck

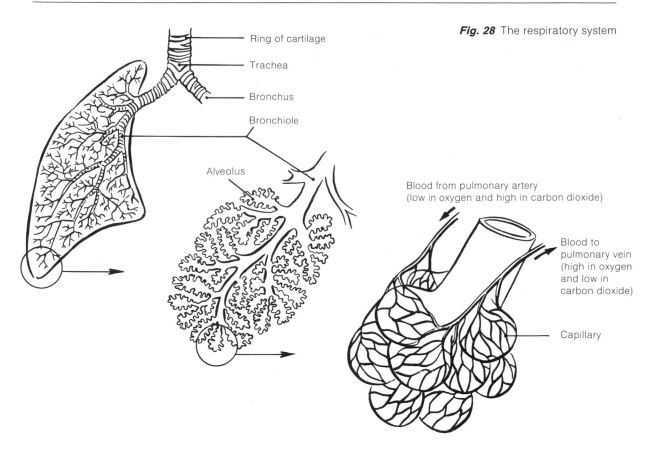

Fig. 28 The respiratory system

Ring of cartilage

Trachea

Bronchus

Bronchiole

Alveolus

Blood from pulmonary artery
(low in oxygen and high in carbon dioxide)

Blood to
pulmonary vein
(high in oxygen
and low in
carbon dioxide)

Capillary

Respiratory problems

No horse or pony is safe from respiratory disease. A recent survey showed that over one-third of a group of young racehorses was unable to work at some time during the year due to respiratory problems. Even a mildly affected horse will not be able to give his best when put under pressure.

Signs of respiratory problems

- nasal discharge – one of the first things the owner may see is mucus outside the stable door in the morning
- coughing – unlike us the horse does not have a well developed cough reflex, so any cough should be taken seriously
- reduced exercise tolerance – the horse may be lethargic and blow more than would be expected

The respiratory system

The respiratory system is designed to draw oxygen from the air into the bloodstream so that energy for life can be produced in the tissues. It starts at the nostrils and ends as a multitude of tiny, thin-walled sacs (alveoli) which are in intimate contact with a dense network of blood capillaries **(figs. 27** and **28)**. An estimated three thousand million alveoli give the lungs a surface area the size of an Olympic swimming pool, allowing oxygen to pass from the lungs into the blood capillaries. The windpipe is prevented from collapse by rings of tough cartilage which keep it open. The tiny bronchioles leading down to the alveoli can collapse, however, sticking together like the fingers of a rubber glove!

Respiratory disease can result for several reasons, as listed overleaf.

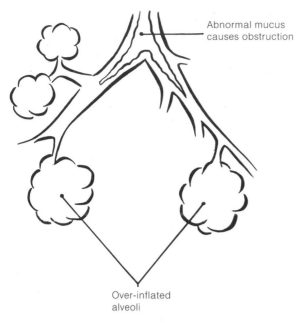

Abnormal mucus causes obstruction

Over-inflated alveoli

Fig. 29 Small-airway disease

- Infection – many horses travel widely to competitions and mix with other horses, and are particularly vulnerable to viral infection. A horse will recover from a simple, uncomplicated viral infection in about a week, but the virus will have damaged the cells lining the airways, so that they are much more susceptible to a secondary bacterial infection.
- Inflammation – local inflammation may follow infection, irritation or allergy. Inflammation leads to swelling of the lining of the airways, reducing their internal diameter and making breathing less efficient **(fig. 29)**.
- Allergy – blood cells attracted by the inflammation may meet fungal spores. This causes the muscle of the airways to go into spasm, reducing the diameter even further. Dead cells and mucus from the inflammatory reaction accumulate, physically blocking the airflow. If left untreated, the horse will eventually suffer from chronic obstructive pulmonary disease and may even become broken-winded.

Treatment of respiratory disease

There is no single 'cure' for respiratory disease, but the following treatments will all aid recovery.

- Rest – in the acute stages of respiratory disease it is important to allow the horse complete rest.
- Getting rid of the mucus – in respiratory disease the cilia that waft away the mucus are reduced in number, and more mucus is produced which is more viscous than usual. Drugs can be used to clear the mucus.
- Relieving the bronchospasm – the small airways of the lungs contract, causing narrowing of the passages, which is known as bronchospasm. This can cause quite severe distress, as the horse will have real difficulty in taking in enough air to breathe; this is equivalent to an asthma attack in humans.

All performance depends on getting maximum oxygen to the tissues, using one system which cannot be seen: the respiratory system. Many horses will have small amounts of airway obstruction because of poor environment and unobserved signs of respiratory disease, and even the smallest obstruction will limit the amount of oxygen getting into the lungs and hence the tissues. Oxygen is essential for efficient energy production and therefore muscle contraction. A lack of oxygen will limit performance, and is known as 'poor performance syndrome'.

Heatstroke and dehydration

The galloping horse produces a temperature rise of 1°C (1·8°F) every three minutes. If there were no temperature regulation in his body, there would be muscle damage within fifteen minutes of starting work, due to the heat generated.

Sweating

The horse can normally lose heat very effectively through the evaporation of sweat from the skin. Heat is used up when the liquid evaporates, leaving the horse's skin cooler. Sweating is most effective when the air temperature and humidity are low and the air is moving. Hot and humid conditions make efficient sweating difficult, as the high water content in the air reduces the evaporation of sweat into the air, so sweat runs off the horse without actually cooling him. Visible sweating means that effective heat loss is not taking place, because the moisture is not evaporating as quickly as it is being produced.

Dehydration

A horse can lose fifteen litres (about three gallons) of sweat in an hour of hard work in hot conditions, and can quickly become dehydrated if this fluid is not replaced. Horse sweat is very rich in electrolytes – mineral salts which must be in correct balance in the body for normal metabolism. Horse sweat contains ten times more sodium and potassium salts than human sweat, and contains even more of these salts than blood plasma. The loss of fluid and electrolytes has several effects.

- As blood volume falls, there is less sweating and the horse becomes hotter.
- As blood volume falls, less oxygen is carried in the blood and the muscles become short of oxygen. Lactic acid is produced, and the horse may tie-up or show colicky pains.
- As the horse heats up he starts to pant. Watch for respiration rates which are higher than the heart rate.
- The loss of essential salts results in muscle tremors, uncoordination and 'thumps', a sign of exhaustion where the horse's heart looks as if it is beating in the flanks.

Assessing dehydration

- The horse is able to store some of the heat produced during work, and it is not uncommon to see temperatures of 39°C (102°F) at the end of Phase C of a three-day event and 40°C (103°F) at the end of Phase D. If the horse's temperature is greater than this (either static or rising), *do not continue to work the horse and cool him as quickly as possible.*
- If a small fold of skin picked up on the horse's neck or shoulder does not return in a normal, supple manner, but takes more than five seconds to flatten out, this indicates dehydration.
- A blood test will confirm dehydration, but it takes time to obtain the results.

Preventing dehydration

The correct preparation of the horse for competition and his management during competition are vital in avoiding these problems.

- Electrolyte replacement during and after competition will help to prevent the horse from dehydrating and will also help him to recover from exertion. Electrolytes are an essential part of the travelling kit. Electrolytes must not be over-fed before or during competition or dehydration may actually be induced.
- Probiotics and enzymes added to the feed will help to overcome the digestive disturbances caused by the fluid changes in the gut, and the irregular feeding that is inevitable.
- Water provision and correct cooling will make the difference between a horse that can compete successfully the next day, and one that stays in his box!
- Before competition do not deprive the horse of water, it is unlikely that he will take a long drink immediately prior to exercise if he has access to water. During competition offer the horse small amounts of water at frequent intervals.

Digestive disorders

Colic

Colic is not a disease, but an abdominal pain which may be caused by a wide variety of disorders. The primary cause of this pain is distension of the stomach or intestines, which may be due to an accumulation of gas, fluid or feed caused by a blockage or improper movement of the gut. Generally the vet should be called as soon as colic is suspected. Hay and feed should be removed and the horse left alone, unless he is so violent as to be in danger of injuring himself **(fig. 30)**, in which case he should be walked and kept warm.

Spasmodic colic Spasmodic colic is caused by spasm of the muscular wall of the intestine. There may be several reasons for this, including damage to the intestinal wall by migrating strongyle larvae, or feeding and drinking too soon after fast work. Affected horses are normally moderately distressed, showing signs of sweating and constantly lying down and getting up. They may look at and kick at their flanks and roll, often getting cast. The pulse rate may rise to seventy to ninety beats per minute, or to over a hundred in severe cases. The respiration rate will increase to up to eighty breaths per minute and the temperature will rise. Horses with spasmodic colic usually pass few droppings, but the condition may come and go quite quickly. If it persists, treatment with a relaxant drug usually relieves the problem rapidly.

Impactive colic This type of colic accounts for about thirty per cent of all colics and is caused by impaction of food material in the large intestine. This often occurs at the pelvic flexure, where the intestine narrows near the pelvis to turn back towards the chest. It may occur because the horse has eaten his bedding,

Fig. 30 A horse suffering from colic may roll violently

or when he goes on to a hay ration when brought in from grass. Affected horses are not normally in a great deal of pain and tend to look dull and off-colour, getting up and down in an uncomfortable manner and rolling more than usual. The vet will insert his hand into the horse's rectum to try to feel where the blockage is; he may give painkillers and also large amounts of liquid paraffin (or a similar agent) via a stomach tube to stimulate gut movement.

Distension (tympanic) colic Distension colic is caused by a build-up of gas in the gut and is usually very painful; horses will sweat and roll violently, often hurting themselves in the process. Gas build-up may occur in front of an impaction, may be due to a twist in the gut or be caused by fermentation of food in the stomach or small intestine.

Intestinal catastrophe Commonly known as twisted gut, this is the most dramatic and serious form of colic. The intestine becomes twisted, telescoped into itself or rotated about its mesentary, all of which obstruct the blood supply. Horses become uncontrollably violent in their agony and immediate veterinary attention is vital if the horse is to survive, as abdominal surgery is necessary.

Predisposing factors

- sudden access to large quantities of rich feed, eg., grass clippings, cereals, fallen apples, lush grass
- changed routine, new stable, new surroundings
- irregular work, changes in feeding routine
- working on full stomach
- exhaustion
- feeding and/or watering too soon after fast work
- mouldy feed

- sudden change of diet
- sharp teeth
- greedy feeders

PREVENTION OF COLIC

As with most problems, good stable management and correct feeding are the answer.

- Feed each horse as an individual, noting his idiosyncrasies.
- Feed concentrates little and often, keeping to regular feeding times – even at weekends!
- Make changes to the diet gradually: do not increase concentrates by more than 0·5 kg (1 lb) a day when building up a ration.
- Use a planned, regular exercise programme.
- Feed good-quality feed and store it away from vermin.
- Keep to your routine, even when away from home.
- Cool the horse thoroughly after strenuous work before allowing him to drink and eat large amounts.
- Have his teeth checked and rasped regularly.
- Stop horses bolting their feed by adding chaff or putting a salt lick or large stones in the manger.
- Keep to a regular, effective worming programme.

Metabolic disorders

Azoturia

Despite intensive investigation, azoturia (also known as tying-up, setfast, exertional rhabdomyolysis and Monday-morning disease) remains a poorly understood disease. It results in muscle stiffness and pain, and these can occur under different circumstances and to a variable degree. The symptoms vary from slight hind-leg stiffness to severe pain and total reluctance to move.

Traditionally, the problem arises soon after the onset of exercise, particularly in fit horses, maintained on a full ration, the day after a rest day. Horses have, however, been known to develop symptoms at grass, in the ten-minute box of a three-day event or during walking exercise. Some horses are prone to recurrent attacks, and highly-strung horses, especially mares, appear to be susceptible. Vitamin E and/or selenium have been implicated, but there is little information to support this and opinion seems to suggest an electrolyte imbalance as being a key factor.

Whatever the cause, the result is muscle damage. Muscle enzymes are released into the bloodstream; these enzymes (CPK and AST) are used to assess the severity of the attack, and the speed at which the levels in the blood fall is used to monitor the rate of recovery from an attack. Lactic acid is also released from the damaged muscle cells, and continuing to work a mildly affected horse can make the condition much worse. It is vital to stop work immediately and get the horse back to his box with as little energy expenditure as possible.

Treatment involves the reduction of pain and inflammation; the horse may need to be sedated and have fluid therapy and it is important to keep him warm. The horse should have only hay and water plus any medicines prescribed by the vet.

Prevention of azoturia is achieved through careful stable management and attention to diet:

- cut the concentrates if the horse has a day off
- warm up and cool down the horse properly
- make sure that the diet contains adequate calcium, phosphorus and salt (sodium chloride)

Lymphangitis

The lymphatic system is a network of fine tubes which collect excess fluid from all parts of the body and return it to the bloodstream. The return of lymph is aided by muscle massage. Too little exercise and excess feeding leads to waterlogging in the tissues and consequently the area becomes swollen (this oedema pits when firm pressure is applied). The lack of exercise means reduced muscle massage, making it more difficult to return the lymph; the rich food disturbs the delicate protein and electrolyte balance and the lymph system is unable to carry away the waste material and excess fluid.

The legs may become filled when the

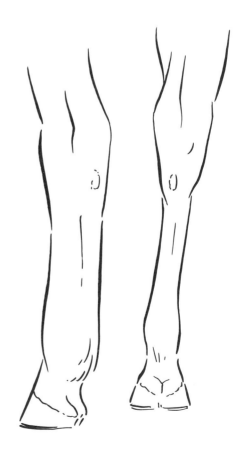

Fig. 31 A near-hind leg swollen due to lymphangitis

walls of the blood and lymph vessels are damaged by toxins, as water passes into the tissue spaces very quickly. The damage may be due to an allergic reaction to a feed or a drug, or may be a direct result of a viral or bacterial reaction. Diets high in protein may aggravate the swellings, with the nutritional element adding to the drainage problem.

Lymphangitis usually occurs in the hind leg and may lead to a permanently enlarged limb **(fig. 31)**. Treatment aims to combat infection and to relieve pain so that controlled exercise can be given. The amount and type of feed must be looked at and changed if necessary.

Mentalstress

Mental stress

Horses often experience considerable mental stress. The show jumper has to perform late at night, for instance, while the dressage horse has to accept strict discipline. Eventers are built to gallop and jump at speed and also asked to do dressage and to show jump; these two disciplines ideally require not only different conformation but, possibly, a different temperament. Consequently the event horse has to contain his natural exuberance and submit to exercises that he finds physically difficult. Very often he will react by 'blowing up', which is a sign of mental stress.

REDUCING MENTAL STRESS

Keeping the supremely fit horse calm enough to perform at his best is a major concern for many riders and trainers. One important aspect of stable management is to keep the system as close to the horse's natural environment as possible.

- **Turn the horse out** as often as possible. Even a short spell of grazing in the field will help a horse to cope with his unnatural stable environment.
- **Keep the diet simple and natural**. The horse evolved to eat grass, and a high proportion of cereals in the diet upsets digestion. Keep hard feed to the minimum.
- **Look after the bugs in the hind gut**. Efficient digestion depends upon maintaining a healthy population of gut bacteria, but, unfortunately, these bugs are upset by many things: too many concentrates, changes in diet, strenuous exercise and erratic feeding times. There are now many products on the market, such as probiotics and enzymes, which enable the horse to be fed in a more natural way. This will help him to maintain a correct internal environment so that he can combat stress, withstand disease and recover effectively from exertion.

- **Feed a balanced diet** containing the correct levels of minerals, vitamins and amino acids. Losses during harvesting, conservation, processing and storage of feeds mean that many concentrates and forages tend to under-supply these micro-nutrients. The horse in light work can cope because the bugs in his large intestine make many B vitamins, but the very fit horse has a greatly reduced gut size and consequently fewer bugs to make B vitamins, and therefore needs a good-quality vitamin, mineral and amino-acid supplement. Some vitamins are claimed to have a calming effect on both horses and humans.
- **Keep the horse pain-free** by ensuring that he is not suffering from minor aches and pains which make his work uncomfortable. Discomfort will cause the horse to be tense, thus increasing the discomfort until he is actively resisting or compensating for the discomfort. Over a period of months this can seriously affect the horse's movement. Keep a sharp look-out for muscle, tendon and ligament problems, and bear in mind that heat is always there for a reason – it should never be ignored.

5
STABLE MANAGEMENT

Any experienced competitor will tell you that competitions are won at home. In other words, feeding, fitness and stable management are as important as schooling and competing in producing a horse that is capable of winning. There is no excuse for competing with a horse in any discipline if he is not fit and healthy enough; riders and trainers need to be aware of the demands that competition will place upon their horse and to train him accordingly. Horses are expensive to keep, and, if we lose valuable time through injury which could have been avoided through a greater understanding, we have only ourselves to blame. The horse is dependent on us to provide the very highest standard of care and attention, and he will then reward us with his best.

Stable management, is a vital part of the preventive health regime of the competition horse. It goes without saying that stable management must be of the highest order, and that the competition groom is a vital member of the team.

Stable management covers all aspects of the daily routine for example the organisation of the yard routine, bedding down and mucking out, grooming, trimming and clipping, bandaging and treating minor ailments.

Daily routine

Keeping a diary is essential in the running of an efficient yard. Worming, vaccinations, teeth-rasping, competition dates and veterinary visits should all be recorded, as well as the daily entries such as the work that the horse did and how he responded to it. In time, this will build up into a detailed picture of a horse's health and fitness which can be used as a reference the following year.

Bedding and mucking out

The stable environment of the competition horse is vital to his health and wellbeing. A top-class human athlete would not shut himself in his bedroom for twenty-two hours a day, inhaling dust and fungal spores, yet this is what many of our equine athletes endure. The bedding that you use should be free of the fungal spores which lead to allergic respiratory problems, and should be as dust-free as possible. This means that straw has become less popular and shavings and paper more popular for bedding horses. Straw has the added disadvantage that horses are inclined to eat it, which may not do their waistlines much good!

No matter what bedding you choose, the bed should be thick enough for the horse to walk and lie on top of the bed, not through it. It is a mistake to fluff up the bed; it should be laid down firm and level or the horse will kick it about and end up standing on the bare floor. The bed must also be clean, as spores will grow on old, mouldy bedding, so make sure that the banks are turned regularly and that soiled bedding is removed **(fig. 32)**. Once a week, if possible, throw the bed up to the walls, sweep the floor thoroughly, disinfect the floor and leave it to dry, to keep the stable fresh.

If your are short of time a semi-deep litter system can work quite adequately; the droppings are skipped out first thing and then regularly during the day, but the base is undisturbed. The wet patches and banks are dug out once or twice a week and the floor swept and disinfected.

Fig. 32 Thorough mucking out is an essential part of the daily routine

Grooming

Grooming is more than just keeping a horse clean; it stimulates the circulation of blood and lymph and gives a shine to the coat by bringing the natural oils to the surface **(fig. 33)**. Grooming is also a chance for you to get to know the horse: both his character and his lumps and bumps, and in this way you will be aware if he is even very slightly off-colour.

Part of the grooming process involves keeping the horse smart: pulling the mane and tail and trimming heels and the jawline. Once the mane and tail have been pulled at the beginning of the competition season, a little attention every other week will mean that your horse always looks neat and tidy: see **(9)** and **(10)** overleaf. Trim the excess feather from the horse's heels but do not clip his legs, as he will need the protection given by that layer of hair to prevent mud fever and to help prevent the entry of thorns. Long, protruding hair can be clipped from the ears, but the fine hair inside the ear should be left, as it protects the ear from flies and rain. Some people trim the whiskers from the muzzle and around the horse's eyes, but remember that these are the horse's feelers, designed to help protect his eyes and muzzle, and ask yourself if it is fair to deprive him of these.

The horse should be quartered every morning before he is exercised. This is a quick brush over the body, removing

Fig. 33 Grooming with a body brush and metal curry comb

stable stains, washing the eyes, nose and dock and picking out the feet – in other words, making the horse presentable and giving you the opportunity to check that all is well.

After the horse has worked he can have a thorough grooming, which may take up to an hour. This means removing all mud, dirt and sweat and then using the body brush to get the coat clean and shining. Wash the eyes, nose and dock, and pick out and dress the feet. The horse may also be strapped, which involves banging the muscles of the neck, shoulders and hindquarters to stimulate the blood supply and promote muscle tone. The legs and shoes should be checked at the same time. The mane should be brushed and laid with a damp brush, the tail fingered out and a tail bandage put on. Baby oil or a spray lotion will help to keep the tail tangle-free and make it easier to shake out those persistent shavings. There is a move away from using oil on the horse's feet, as it is now thought that using a hoof moisturizer allows water to move in and out of the hoof, preventing it from becoming either too brittle or too soft.

At some stage you may wish to bathe your horse. Be sure to choose a warm day, and if in doubt do not wash his head or he may catch a chill if the weather changes suddenly. Once he is washed and thoroughly rinsed, remove excess water from his body with a sweat scraper and towel-dry his head, body and legs, put on a sweat sheet and walk him round until he is dry. Many horses are routinely hosed down after work, even in the winter. If you do this, you must ensure that your horse's legs are dried each time, or he will end up with sore, cracked heels. Pink skin is particularly vulnerable, so use baby oil or cream to protect the heels and keep the skin soft. The cream we use to protect our own hands can also be used on the horse's pasterns and heels.

THE GROOMING KIT

The grooming kit consists of several items each of which have a specific use;

- Dandy brush – coarse and stiff bristles, used for removing mud and dried sweat from the body and limbs. Not be used on the head, on thin-skinned or clipped horse or on the tail. Very useful for grass-kept horses.
- Body brush – shorter and softer bristles to remove grease from the coat. Used with a circular action followed by a long stroke to remove the dirt. Used to clean the horse's head.
- Curry comb – used to clean the body brush which is swept over the curry comb every four or five strokes. The accumulated dirt is tapped out of the curry comb at regular intervals.
- Water brush – long soft bristles, used to dampen mane and tail before plaiting or applying a tail bandage. Also used to scrub the legs or feet clean.
- Sponge – one for the eyes, nose and lips, one for the dock and sheath (these should be marked so that they are not mixed up) and a large sponge for washing the horse down or removing stable stains.
- Wisp – a stuffed leather pad or a traditional wisp made from a length of twisted hay or straw used to strap the horse.
- Mane comb – a metal or plastic comb for combing out the mane, for pulling the mane and tail and for preparing the mane and tail for plaiting.
- Stable rubber – a linen cloth used slightly damp to wipe over the horse at the end of grooming to remove any dust.
- Hoof pick – used to remove mud and stones from the foot and may have a brush on one end to thoroughly clean the underside of the hoof.
- Sweat scraper – use to remove excess sweat or water from the horse's coat after exercise.

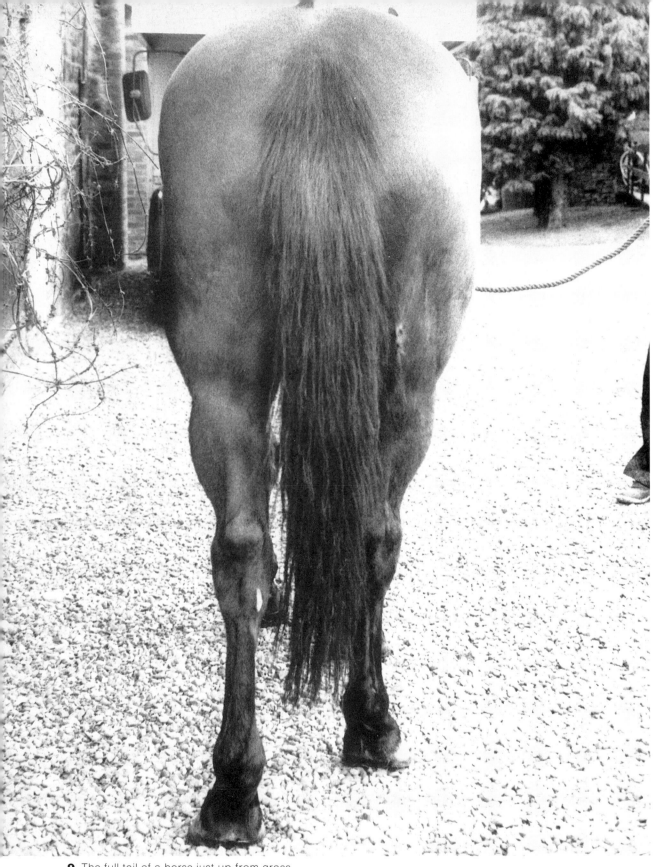

9 The full tail of a horse just up from grass

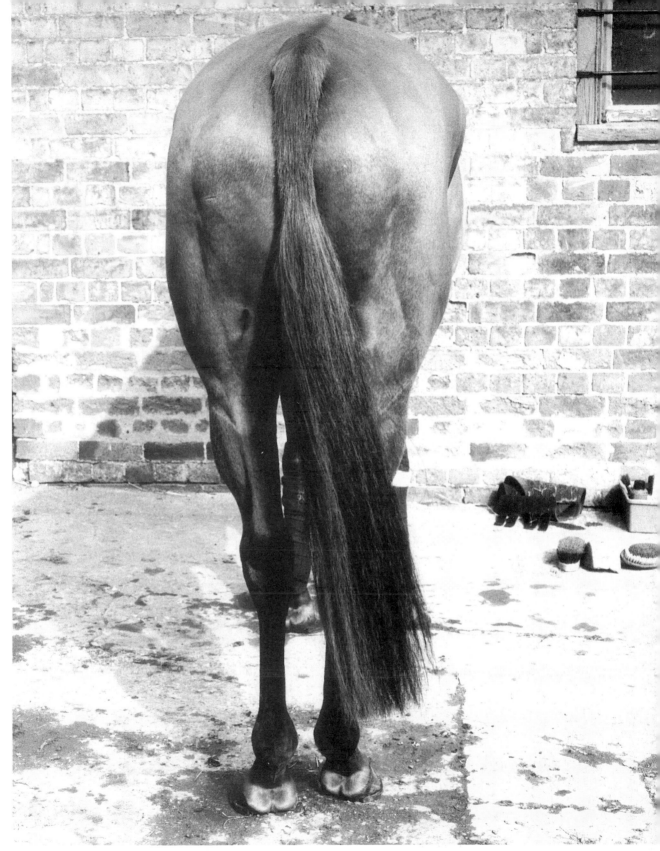

10 The same horse with a neatly pulled, trimmed and washed tail. Avoid brushing the tail, or it will lose hairs and become thin

Turning out

The natural place for a horse is outside, and the competition horse will benefit both mentally and physically from a regular turn-out in the paddock. Unfortunately, paddocks can be dangerous places, and if the horse has not been out for a long time he may charge around wildly. For this reason, try to make turning out part of your routine so that the horse will be unlikely to hurtle round and damage himself. If it is not possible to turn him out, at least let him loose in the school or ménage to have a buck and a roll, and be a horse instead of a means of transport for humans!

Paddocks should be safely fenced and free of hazards such as litter and pot-holes, with a safe, adequate water supply. It may be sensible to turn the horse out in front boots for protection, but take care that these do not rub, particularly if he has a bony lump on his leg, such as a splint. If you leave a headcollar (halter) on the horse, make sure that it is an old leather one which will break if it gets caught on something; nylon headcollars do not break.

Bandaging

Any competition horse depends on sound legs. Checking your horse's legs should be as instinctive as closing a stable door behind you; you should know how your horse's legs normally look and feel, so that you can spot any abnormal heat and swelling immediately. There is always a reason for heat in a horse's leg, and this warning sign must not be ignored. Instead, the horse's workload must be reduced in intensity until the legs are back to normal. If the horse is worked as usual, severe damage may be done. The horse's legs are protected and supported by boots and bandages, but bandages must be applied correctly, or they can cause real damage. Following a few simple rules should help to avoid problems.

- The bandage must be rolled correctly and firmly. Ensure that the tapes are flat and rolled to the inside.
- Never apply bandages too tightly.
- Ensure that the tension is even with no wrinkles. The tapes must not be tied more tightly than the bandage.
- The bandage should be put on anti-clockwise on the left legs and clockwise on the right legs so that the presssure runs from bone to tendon, not the other way round.
- Any padding used under the bandage should run in the same direction as the bandage. The edge of the padding must not lie on the tendon.
- The tapes should be tied on the outside of the leg, not on the tendon or front of the leg.
- The ends of the tape should be tucked in and secured with insulating tape, a safety pin or sewing.

The padding used under bandages comes in various types. One form commonly used is gamgee (cotton wool in a gauze cover), which is clean and gives good protection, especially if wrapped round the leg twice. Gamgee is expensive and easily soiled, although, if the edges are blanket-stitched, it can be washed and re-used.

An alternative is fibagee, a type of felt-covered foam which is durable and easy to wash. American leg-wraps are thick and durable, giving good protection, but are not suitable for use under exercise bandages. Several layers of cotton wool can be used straight off the roll under a support bandage. Hay or straw can be used under loosely applied stable bandages for thatching and drying legs. Bandages have different uses, depending on the materials

Fig. 34 Fitting a stable bandage

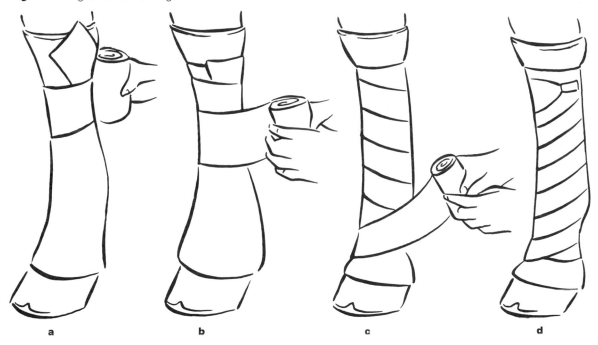

a   b   c   d

a Leaving a flap, start the bandage just below the knee or hock, ensuring that the gamgee (or other padding) extends from knee or hock to coronet

b Fold down the flap and bandage over it. Overlap half the width of the bandage at each turn

c Bandage down to the coronet and back up the leg

d Finish near the top of the bandage and fasten. The fastening may be velcro (as here) or tapes, which should be tied at the side of the leg to avoid putting pressure on the bone or tendon

PUTTING ON A STABLE BANDAGE (Fig. 34)

- Place the lining round the leg. When you have finished, there should be 1·5 cm ($\frac{1}{2}$ in) of lining showing above and below the bandage.
- If the bandage is long enough, start just below the knee or hock, leaving a 10 cm (4 ins) flap (**a**). If the bandage is short, start just above the fetlock (this may be preferable, as you will be bandaging upward, towards the heart).
- Fold down the flap and bandage over it to secure the bandage. Overlap half the width of the bandage at each turn (**b**).
- Bandage down to the coronet and up again (**c**).
- Finish near the top of the bandage. Fasten the velcro, or tie the tapes in a neat bow and tuck in the ends (**d**).
- For travelling, tuck the gamgee under the heels of the shoes.

A support (stretch) bandage – used if the horse has a tendon injury, for example – is applied in the same way.

used and the way in which they are applied.

Stable bandages

Stable bandages are used for warmth, for drying off wet legs, for protection, as support for a sound leg which may be taking more strain than usual and to keep dressings in place. These bandages are usually made of wool, or synthetic material which may have thermal properties, and should be 10–12 cm (4–5 ins) wide and 2–2·5 m (7–8 ft) long. They are always

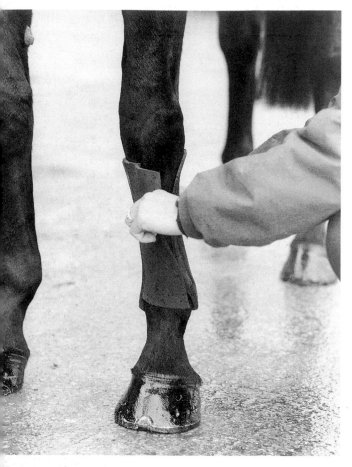

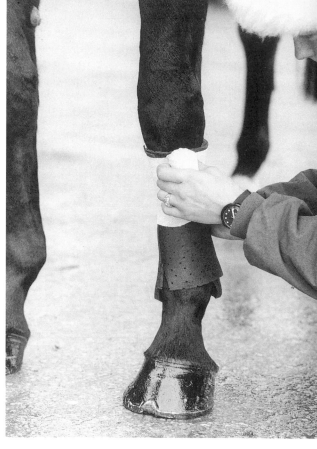

11 Place the tendon protector around the leg with the flap overlapping to the rear. Each horse should have his own protectors, trimmed to fit that horse's legs

12 Start the bandage at the top, applying it from front to back, quite firmly

applied with padding underneath. If being used for poulticing or support with an elastic bandage, double-thickness gamgee should be used. When using a stable bandage for protection while travelling, ensure that the gamgee comes well over the knee and coronet.

Exercise bandages

Exercise bandages do not really ease the strain on the horse's tendons, but they are very effective at protecting the leg in a similar way to a boot. A stretch bandage such as elastic, crêpe or Vetwrap, 7·5–10 cm (3–4 ins) wide and 1·8–2 m (6–7 ft)

long is used, and it is also essential to use a lining, such as gamgee or a tendon protector **(11)** to **(17)**. An exercise bandage is fitted as previously outlined except for the following points:

- apply the bandage more firmly
- leave a longer flap for security when starting the bandage
- the bandage runs from below the knee to the fetlock joint, finishing just above the ergot
- the bandage tapes should be sewn or taped for security
- the bandage should not be left on for long periods

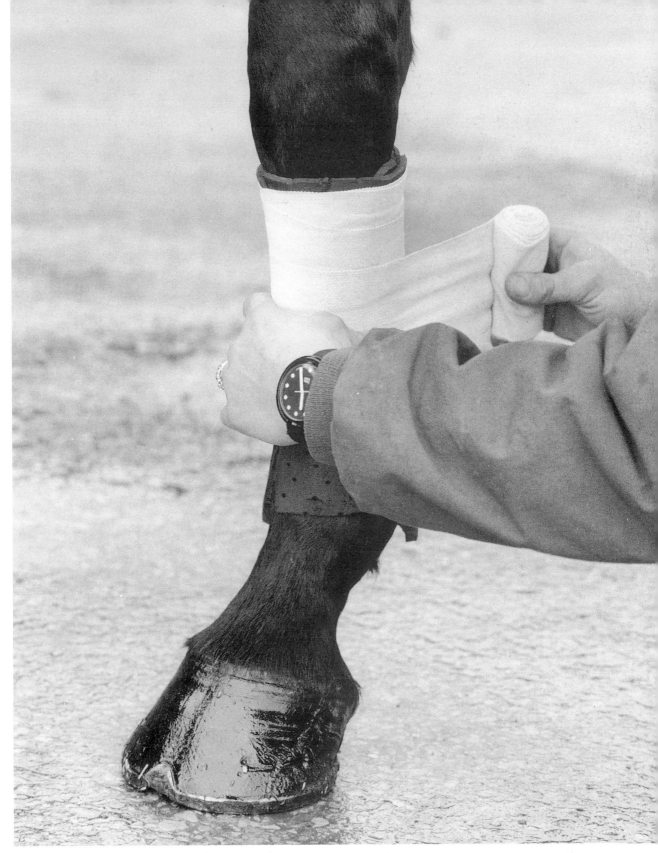

13 To ensure even tension, hold the front of the leg and unroll the bandage before laying it around the horse's leg

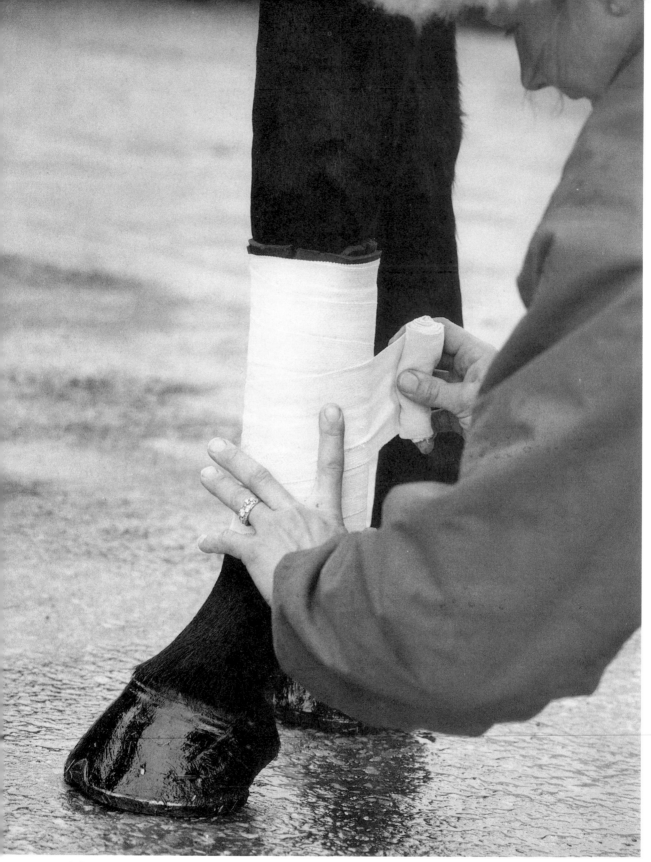

14 Ease out any wrinkles with a finger as you go

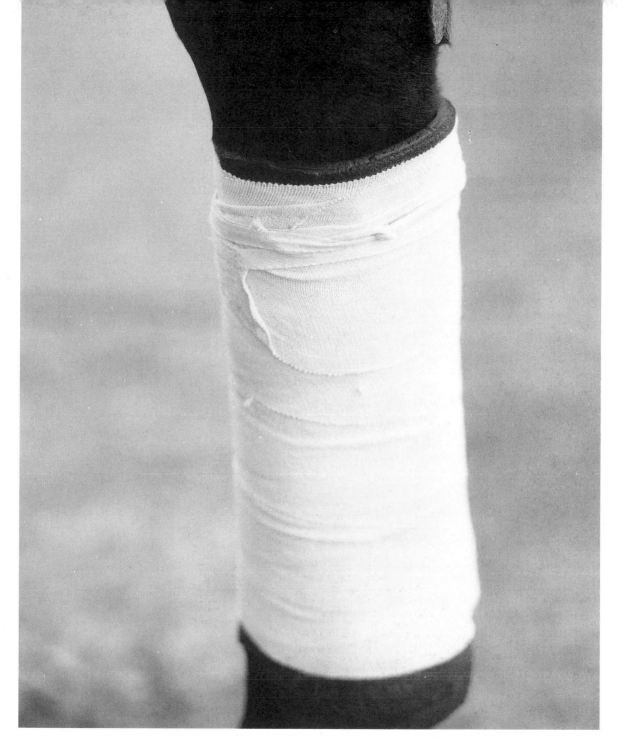

- overlap two-thirds of the bandage at each turn
- do not remove the bandages from a tired horse until he has recovered, as he needs the support

Bandages are removed by untying the tapes and unwinding the bandage by passing it quickly from hand to hand. The legs

15 Finish on the outside of the leg with flat tapes and a neat knot, with the ends tucked away. The fastening should be almost invisible!

should then be rubbed briskly upward, towards the heart. The used bandage should be shaken out, brushed or washed, and re-rolled with the tapes at the centre.

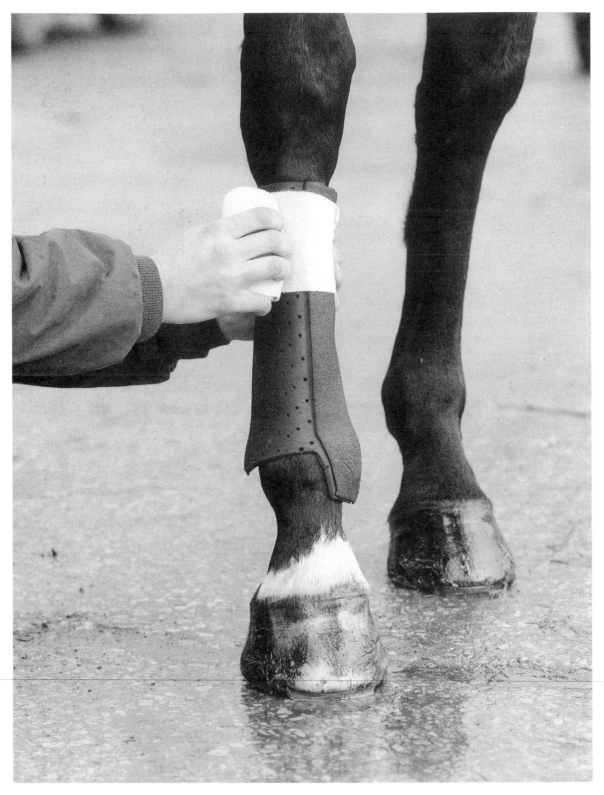

16 Bandaging a hind leg. The protector must extend well down over the inside of the fetlock joint. Start the bandage as in **(12)** on page 78, holding the free end firmly to prevent it from slipping

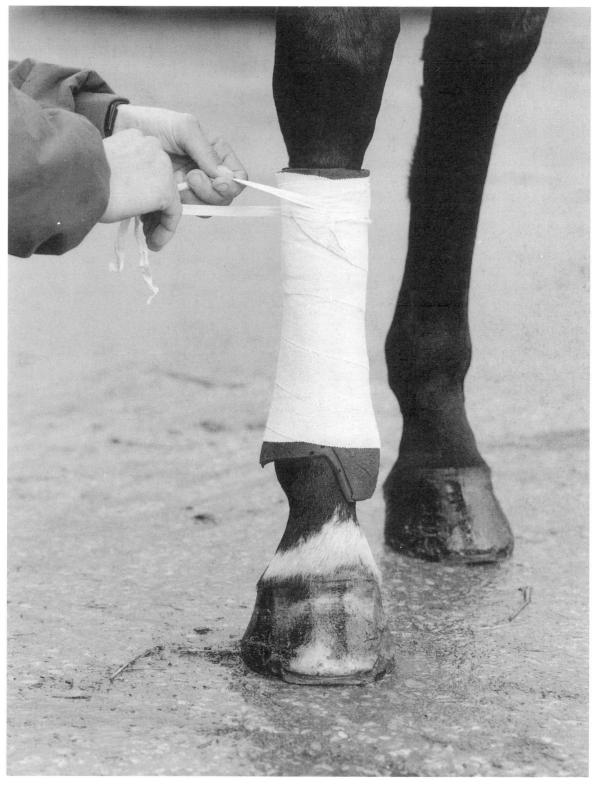

17 When finishing the bandage, flatten the tapes between your thumb and forefinger.
Ensure that the tapes are no tighter than the bandage

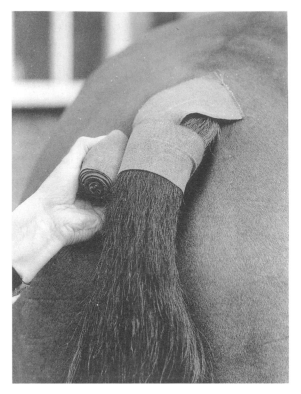

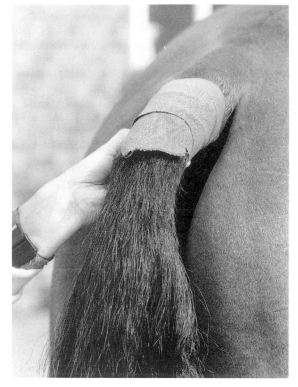

18 Starting a tail bandage. Begin slightly below the top of the tail, leaving a flap to fold down

19 Bandage to the top of the tail, incorporating the flap

Tail bandage

Tail bandages are made of crêpe or elastic, 5–7·5 cm (2–3 ins) wide and 1·5–1·6 m (5–6 ft) long. They are used to enhance the appearance of a horse's tail, to protect the tail or for safety, for example when covering and clipping.

Horses that sit on their tails when travelling may push the tail bandage down and rub their tail, these horses will need to be fitted with a tail guard (24). For short journeys the tail guard is fitted over the bandage, but for longer journeys the tail guard is used alone. If a tail bandage is put on too tightly or left on for too long, for example overnight or for a very long journey it can damage the dock. The pressure can result in the underneath of the dock becoming sore and tail hair falling out. Sometimes horses are left with permanently white tail hairs.

PUTTING ON A TAIL BANDAGE

- Hold up the tail or put it over your shoulder.
- Place the bandage under the tail, leaving a 10 cm (4 ins) flap (**18**).
- Secure the bandage and then make one or two turns, as high up as possible (**19**).
- Overlap about half the bandage at each turn or criss-cross the bandage.
- Bandage down to the end of the dock.
- Tie the tapes to the side, to prevent them from pressing into the dock should the horse sit on his tail while travelling (**20**).

Tail bandages should stay on for no more than four hours. They should be applied firmly, but never too tightly.

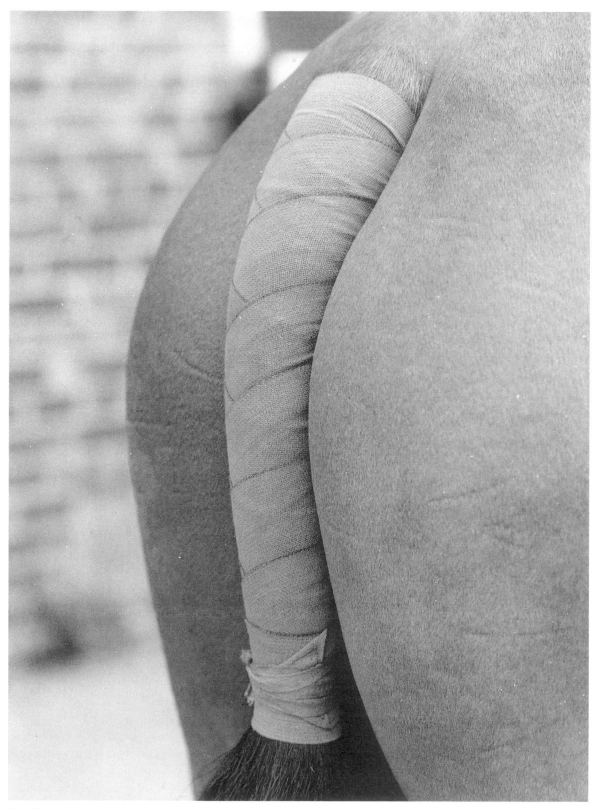

20 The bandage can be criss-crossed for extra security

Shoeing

The farrier is an essential part of the team involved in getting and keeping the competition horse on the road. He is a busy and skilled man, and will appreciate a horse owner who books him well in advance and does not wait until the shoes are hanging off, trying to get a few extra days of wear, and then phoning with a plea for urgent attention because a shoe has been lost. Discuss your horse's requirements with the farrier, as he may be able to fit remedial shoes to correct problems such as poor foot shape, tripping, brushing or over-reaching.

A competition horse is likely to need stud holes in his shoes; fill the holes with greased cotton wool to prevent the tread from being damaged, or small stones becoming wedged in the holes. Tungsten-tipped nails are useful as they will help to stop him from slipping on tarmac.

Have a spare set of shoes made before going to a competition, so that, if a shoe has to be replaced quickly, you already have one that fits at hand. Note the state of the shoes every time you pick out the horse's feet, looking for excess wear, raised clenches, the foot over-growing the shoe, or the shoe starting to spread. Also bear in mind the work that the horse has to do in the near future and the proximity of the next competition – will the shoes last?

Too many horse owners judge the farrier merely by whether or not the shoes stay on, however, hoof balance is an essential ingredient to good shoeing. The balanced foot is one that is trimmed and shod to allow the forces during movement to be directed along the lower leg and foot as evenly as possible, taking into account the horse's natural conformation. If the stresses of galloping and jumping are taken equally then the horse is less likely to suffer tendon or ligament problems.

The first-aid kit

The first-aid kit should be kept in a small, clean, waterproof box and contain the items needed to deal with minor injuries, such as superficial cuts and grazes, kicks, thorns, over-reaches and wire cuts, and to care for the horse before the vet arrives. The following are useful inclusions in the first-aid kit.

- Antiseptic for cleaning wounds.
- Wound powder or spray for use if the wound is to be left open: this prevents infection and dries the wound. Use a fly-repellent powder in the summer.
- An antiseptic ointment, for use on cracked heels and mud fever, and a healing cream to use on dressings before bandaging a wound.
- Crêpe bandages to give support and slight pressure, and adhesive bandages to hold on dressings. Bandages must be applied with light, even pressure, with adequate padding and no wrinkles.
- Sterile, non-adherent dressings to place over a wound before bandaging.
- Cotton wool for cleaning wounds.
- Gamgee for padding under bandages.
- Scissors with curved, blunt ends for cutting hair from the edges of a wound, and scissors with straight blades for cutting tapes and bandages.
- Hot poultices to increase blood supply, draw out infection and encourage abcesses to burst, and cold poultices to decrease inflammation and bruising.
- A thermometer and petroleum jelly.
- Salt to add to water for wound-cleaning.

The contents of the first aid kit must be checked regularly and items such as wound sprays and powders that have reached their "sell-by" date replaced and low stocks of commonly used items topped up. All the contents must be kept scrupulously clean.

Wounds and minor injuries

The competition horse is very prone to injury from falls, becoming tangled in fencing and hitting jumps. The wound may be open or closed: open wounds involve skin damage, while closed wounds are bruises, sprains and ruptures.

Open wounds

Open wounds fall into distinct categories: incised wounds, abrasions, lacerations and tears, and puncture wounds. Incised wounds have clean, straight edges and often bleed freely **(fig. 35)**. There is usually little bruising, and these wounds normally heal quickly. A typical incised wound is caused by surgical incision or a cut by metal or glass.

Abrasions are very superficial skin wounds, such as saddle sores or grazes from coming down on the road. These should be thoroughly cleaned and lightly bandaged.

Lacerated wounds have torn edges and an irregular shape, with some bruising and a variable amount of bleeding. Any flaps of skin usually die and may be cut off to aid healing. These wounds are commonly caused by wire and protruding nails.

Puncture wounds are often more serious than they look. There may only be a small skin opening, but the flesh will be penetrated to a varying depth, causing splinters and bacteria to be carried deep into the wound and resulting in infection. The skin wound may be so small that it is overlooked. Puncture wounds may be caused by bites, stakes and treading on nails, and carry with them the risk of tetanus. They must be poulticed to draw out infection, and encouraged to drain so that they heal from the inside out.

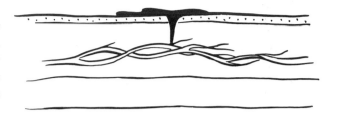

Trauma to tissue; skin is broken; bleeding begins

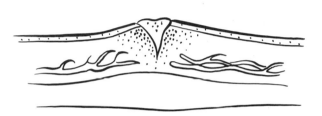

Exudates enter the area from the engorged blood vessels, causing redness and swelling. Swelling helps to stop the bleeding and permits the lymphocytes to 'police' the wound

A scab forms and fibrous adhesions form from the exudates. The tissues gradually return to normal and blood vessels begin to invade the area

Fig. 35 The healing process of an open wound

Treatment of open wounds

1. Control the bleeding.
2. Clean the wound.
3. Promote rapid healing.

Slight bleeding will help to clean the wound. If the bleeding is minor, clean the wound and apply a dressing, which will help to stop the bleeding. If the bleeding is more serious, call the vet and apply pressure to the wound while you are waiting for him to arrive. Use a clean dressing and hold it firmly to the wound. If the injury is on a leg, put a pressure bandage on the limb over layers of gamgee, removing the pressure as soon as the bleeding has stopped. It is advisable to avoid the use of tourniquets, as they can cause more problems than they solve.

Hosing is the best way to clean the wound initially, especially if it is large and dirty. Avoid too great a water pressure as this will drive dirt into the wound, and take care that the surrounding skin and hair are also clean. This process should take about fifteen to twenty minutes to complete. After hosing, the wound should be bathed with a dilute solution of mild skin antiseptic or salt; use warm water and a syringe to direct the water, or swabs of clean cotton wool (these should be discarded each time, not returned to the water). It may be necessary to clip or shave the surrounding area so that effective cleaning can take place.

The next step is to debride the wound, or to remove foreign bodies and dead and damaged tissue which will delay healing. This may be a job for the vet, and the horse may need to have a twitch applied or to be given a tranquilliser. Debridement may have to be repeated, as some tissue may die despite correct treatment.

Good wound drainage is essential for the correct healing of puncture wounds and for wounds where there has been extensive loss of tissue. These types of wounds are best left open, and the vet may have to create a second skin opening to allow fluid and debris to leave the wound.

The healing process starts immediately after injury, and wounds can heal in several ways, depending on the type and site of the injury. Healing by 'first intention' only occurs in non-contaminated incised wounds where the edges of the wound can be brought together. If a wound needs stitching, this should be done as soon as possible for successful healing. Stitches stay in for a minimum of ten days, and the wound should be bandaged if it is on a limb.

A wound is said to heal by second intention if it undergoes granulation. First the wound will contract as much as possible, and then the skin cells multiply and migrate across the surface of the wound to form new tissue. The more contraction that can occur, the smaller the area that has to be covered by new cells. Wounds on the horse's body cause little scarring, as the skin is loose and wound contraction is extensive. There is little or no loose skin on the horse's lower legs, and this results in the formation of proud flesh. Proud flesh inhibits healing as it prevents new skin from covering the area, but can be prevented by pressure-bandaging and immobilizing the area. Once proud flesh has formed, it has to be removed by surgery or caustic solutions such as copper sulphate or silver nitrate.

The next step is to dress the clean wound. Bandages help to immobilize the area, to keep it clean and to protect the wound from further damage. The pressure exerted by the bandage helps to control swelling and bleeding. Some wounds, however, are best left open and dressed with powder or spray, and many parts of the horse's body are quite impossible to bandage! All the dressings used should be non-adhesive with sufficient padding, and not applied too tightly.

Depending on the severity and type of injury, the vet may prescribe antibiotics, painkillers and anti-inflammatory drugs for the horse.

It is difficult to accelerate the healing process, but it is very easy to delay it. Ensure that the wound is kept clean, drains adequately and does not become infected. Other factors affecting healing may not be within our power to alter, such as the blood supply to the wound, its position and the age of the horse.

Closed wounds

Closed wounds, such as bruises caused by kicks and falls, involve bleeding and swelling without breaking of the skin, and are characterized by swelling, heat and pain. They are treated by immobilizing the area and using cold hosing or ice packs to draw out the heat and ease the pain. Once the area is cool, heat treatments can be used to help the absorption of excess fluid so that the swelling is reduced.

Bruises received by horses are often very difficult to immobolise or bandage and depending on the position and severity of the injury the horse may be better turned out to wander round and unstiffen and reduce the swelling rather than be kept in his stable. After the initial heat and swelling has reduced hot fomentations can be used to help the healing process. Fomenting is a way of applying heat to an area that cannot be poulticed. Firstly dissolve 227g (8oz) of salt in hot water and then place this in a clean bucket and add cold water until the water is a comfortable temperature. A towel or wad of material is soaked in the water, wrung out and then placed over the bruised area. As soon as the towel cools the procedure is repeated for up to 20 minutes. The bucket is topped up with hot water as necessary. This should be repeated two or three times a day until the swelling has subsided.

STABLE-MANAGEMENT POINTS TO REMEMBER

- The worming programme (see page 59) must be planned so that the horse is wormed every six to eight weeks, but major competition dates should be avoided.
- Routine vaccinations should be given according to current veterinary practice and as required by competition rules, as outlined on page 57. The dates of vaccinations must be planned around the competition season. The necessary vaccinations are likely to include: tetanus toxoid, Eastern and Western encephalomyelitis, Venezuelan encephalitis and influenza. International competitors will need a recent negative Coggin's test certificate against equine infectious anaemia.
- The horse's teeth should be inspected every six months by a vet or horse dentist and rasped if necessary. Some horses may need their teeth checked more often than this.
- The horse's passport must be completed by a vet who is not the owner of the horse; it is proof of the horse's identity and must be completed correctly according to current regulations. It will give an exact description of the horse and the dates of his vaccinations. For horses travelling abroad, it also gives details of immunization programmes and blood tests. In order to enter many competitions and shows, or to stable a horse at a racecourse, any horse without a passport must have an identification and vaccination certificate completed by a veterinary surgeon.

Part 2
CARE
OF THE
HORSE DURING
COMPETITION

6

PREPARATION AND TRAVELLING

The week before the competition

You are likely to have entered for your competition long before this time, and the week before the competition is the time for those finishing touches: the mane and tail should be tidied up and the horse clipped if necessary. All tack and equipment must be examined thoroughly and repaired or replaced if necessary, any items missing from your checklist must be purchased, and you should ensure that no medications are out of date. The horse should be shod with stud holes as necessary, and the farrier asked to check that the horse's spare set of shoes still fits correctly. The numnahs (saddle pads), boots and rugs, etc. which are being taken to the competition should be clean and in good repair.

The horse should be fit by this time. If he is not fit, working him hard in the last week will not suddenly get him ready for the competition. The one-day-event horse should follow the four-day programme already outlined, so that the work in the last week looks like this (remember to work your programme backwards from the competition so that fast work days fall in an appropriate place):

Day 7: day off
Day 6: hack and school
Day 5: hack, school and jump
Day 4: fast work
Day 3: hack only
Day 2: hack and school
Day 1: hack, school and jump
One-day horse trial

The programme before leaving for a three-day event would be similar, except that the horse is likely to travel to the event the day before the preliminary vetting. The pre-event programme would therefore look something like this:

Day 4: fast work
Day 3: hack only
Day 2: hack and school
Day 1: hack, school and jump
Travel to event; hack and school
Vetting
First day of dressage
Second day of dressage; short gallop as a pipe opener
Speed-and-endurance day
Second vetting and show jumping

There is no point in working the horse extra hard in the week prior to a competition; he should be fit enough and too much work may tire him.

The day before the competition

If you are staying overnight before or after your competition, it is essential to be properly organized; clean equipment should be gathered together and packed. The equipment needed will vary slightly depending on the discipline (see the Appendix on pages 170–2) but the following list gives the general requirements for most situations.

The horse should be thoroughly groomed. If the weather permits, it may be possible to bathe him, and you will need to wash his mane, tail and any white socks. If his whiskers and bridle path are trimmed, a last trim will prevent a 'designer-stubble' look.

Equipment should be listed and ticked off as loaded, to prevent vital items from being overlooked. Simple containers such as plastic washing baskets will make loading and unloading easier, but they should not be too large or too heavy as this makes handling awkward. Containers should have an easily read list of contents so that items can be located quickly. Feed is best packed in individual, labelled paper sacks; this is helpful if the horse has to be fed during the journey. Filled water containers and buckets should be packed so that they are accessible during the journey for watering the horse.

You may be very busy but it is important that the horse's routine is disturbed as little as possible. Some horses are very sensitive to the air of anticipation preceding a competition and become agitated or refuse to eat as soon as they have their mane and tail washed. If this is the case try to make the preparation more subtle – clean the horse two days before competition or, if time permits, on the morning before you travel. Do not forget your own equipment – clothing, registration documents and maps should all be sorted out.

EQUIPMENT FOR THE COMPETITION

- stable tools, muck skip, muck sack
- shavings or paper bedding (if not provided by competition organizers)
- two haynets
- two water buckets and full water carrier
- feed bowl
- pre-packed concentrate feeds, clearly labelled: for example, 'Monday lunch'
- soaked sugar-beet pulp (if fed)
- hay or haylage
- supplements (e.g., electrolytes)
- grooming kit, including extra sponges, towels, sweat scraper, hoof oil and fly spray
- plaiting kit
- spare set of shoes, studs and fitting kit
- tack-cleaning kit
- spare rugs and blankets
- two sweat sheets or coolers
- waterproof rugs
- stable bandages and gamgee or wraps
- passport/vaccination certificate
- rule book and details of entry
- rider/driver equipment

Other essential items:

- tack (depending on horse and competition)
- bandages, brushing boots, over-reach boots (plus spares)
- spare girth, leathers, stirrups and reins
- spare headcollar (halter) and rope
- hole punch
- lungeing equipment
- travelling equipment for horse
- human first-aid kit
- equine first-aid kit (see page 86), to include scissors, cotton wool, crêpe bandages, gamgee, salt, wound dressings and sprays, ready-to-use poultice, leg coolant

Procedure before travelling

All vehicles should be regularly serviced to prevent unnecessary problems. It is essential to check the floor of all horse transport on a regular basis, as wooden floors can rot and break. The towing vehicle or horse box should have adequate oil, water and petrol. The battery, lights and tyre pressures should also be checked. You should always travel with the papers that you may need in an emergency: insurance and registration documents and your driver's licence. Up-to-date maps are also a good idea, along with small first-aid kits for both horses and humans.

The trailer tyres must be checked. The trailer may stand unused for several weeks, and the tyres may look safe until the trailer is hitched up and the horses loaded, whereupon the tyres may look very flat! Once the trailer is hitched, the coupling hitch and safety chain or wire should be checked **(fig. 36)**, along with the indicators, side lights, brake lights and internal light. Before moving off, the groom's door should be closed, the jockey wheel and cables secured clear of the ground, and a final check made to ensure that the ramps are securely fastened. If you are hiring transport, do not assume that all these checks have already been carried out.

After travelling, the vehicle should be skipped out, damp bedding removed, the remaining bedding thrown to the front and the floor swept thoroughly and left to dry. Depending on the construction of the vehicle, the floor should be scrubbed and hosed, and rubber matting lifted regularly.

Fig. 36 Ensure that the trailer is safely hitched. The safety chain or wire should be attached to the brake, in case the trailer comes away from the towing vehicle

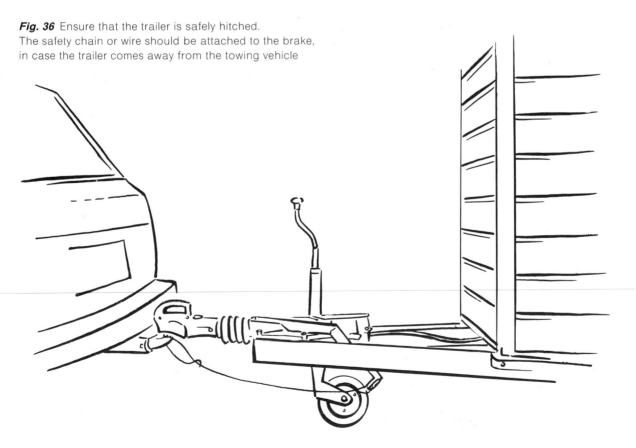

Transporting horses

Before setting off, anyone new to driving a horse box or trailer should have a practice run with an empty vehicle. Once under-way, follow the guidelines below:

- avoid sudden braking, rapid acceleration and fast cornering
- use the gears in conjunction with the brakes to decelerate gently into a corner or halt, and pull away or out of the bend steadily
- pay attention when travelling over a rough or uneven surface
- remember that horses can become frightened if transported badly
- overhanging branches and uncut hedges along narrow lanes may frighten horses as they bang against the sides of the vehicle – take care!
- trailers towed too fast can start to sway and become so unstable that they jack-knife or turn over, particularly down-hill, or in windy or slippery conditions
- a speed of 30–35 m.p.h. (48–56 km) is acceptable, although there are no hard-and-fast rules

Loading

Walking into a small, dark, enclosed space goes against all the horse's instincts, and teaching a horse to load requires exper-ience and forethought on the part of the handler to give him confidence.

The position of the vehicle is important; park it alongside a wall or solid fence, avoiding slippery surfaces. If the horse is being loaded from a field, try to site the vehicle so that the gate can be closed behind the horse to surround him on three sides. The box or trailer should be cor-rectly prepared: there should be short loops of breakable string through the tie-up rings, the floor should be bedded down

and the horse given as much room as possible by swinging back and securing the partitions. If the horse is being loaded for the first time, it may be better to remove the partitions. The horse can also be encouraged to load by opening the jockey door or the front of a front-unload trailer.

The ramp must be level and firm (wedges may be needed to achieve this). The angle of a box ramp may be lessened if the box is parked down a slope, so that the ramp opens up the slope. The slope on a trailer ramp is much less steep, which some horses find easier initially.

A covered school is an ideal place for loading a difficult horse. The vehicle can be parked so that the ramp opens into the school, with any gaps filled with straw bales. Horses tend to associate the school with discipline, and the enclosed space will encourage them to load. Should the horse prove naughty, he is less likely to injure himself on the school surface than on concrete.

A horse which is being taught to load should be rewarded with feed or hay once in the trailer, and then unloaded. Once this has been repeated a couple of times and the horse associates the trailer or box with a pleasurable experience, he can be taken for a short journey. Soon he will look forward to the trailer or box as something associated with fun outings! Remember that the time spent in training a horse to load is never wasted, as a difficult loader is a menace to himself and his handlers.

Procedure

The assistant stands quietly by the side of the ramp, taking care not to put the horse off by staring at him as he approaches the vehicle. The handler stands by the horse's shoulder, well away from the vehicle, and quietly leads the horse forward and

straight up the ramp **(21)**. If the horse is reluctant, he should not be pulled, as this will only make him pull back even more. If the horse stops, give him a titbit or a pat on the neck, look ahead and walk forward. Horses are often reassured if they see their handler go in before them. If the horse pulls backwards, move back with him – do not initiate a battle and upset him.

Once the horse is inside, stand by him while the partition or breeching strap is secured. Do not duck under the front bar, as if the horse pulls back you may be hurt. When lifting the ramp, the assistant should stand to one side in case the horse rushes out as the ramp is going up. The horse can then be tied to a loop of string placed through the tie-ring. He should be tied so that he cannot swing round, but not so tightly that he feels restrained and cannot balance himself.

If you are loading a horse without an assistant, it is useful to use a lunge line; this can be threaded through the tie-ring

21 The handler quietly leads the horse forward and straight up the ramp *(Kit Houghton Photography)*

once the horse has loaded. As you move behind the horse to secure the breeching strap or partition, the lunge line can be held taut to encourage the horse to stay still.

Coping with a shy loader

A horse can be difficult to load for many reasons: he may be reluctant to leave his friends, or be frightened of the enclosed space or a steep ramp, and often horses handled by inexperienced people will have 'got away' with refusing to load. Good handling will overcome these problems fairly easily, but if the horse has memories of a bad journey or forceful loading, it may take a long time before he loads confidently.

It is important to be prepared, as loading a reluctant horse can be dangerous and safety precautions must be taken. The handler must be experienced and strong enough to keep the horse straight on the ramp and to prevent him whipping round and getting loose. Assistants and handlers must be suitably dressed with strong, non-slip shoes, gloves and protective head-gear. The vehicle should be sited as described on page 95, with plenty of straw on the ramp, and the horse should be well-protected by suitable clothing. A lunge whip and two lunge lines should be handy, along with some food to tempt the horse. A strong horse may need to wear a snaffle bridle for control, although generally a lunge cavesson with a lunge line attached to the centre ring is adequate.

The horse should be led to the ramp, held still, patted and allowed to sniff the ramp. If he is quiet, an assistant can lift one front leg and then the other, and place the horse's foot on the ramp. If the horse moves back, follow him and start again. An alternative method is to attach a lunge line to each side of the vehicle. The lines are held by two assistants and crossed behind the horse's quarters to encourage him forward (fig. 37). Some horse's resent this and may rear, so the assistants must be quick to anticipate problems and slacken the lines if necessary.

If the horse is not a kicker, two people can link fingers behind his quarters and push him up the ramp, and if he is still reluctant, another person can lift one foot at a time. Obviously there is some danger in this method, but the closer you get to the horse's hindquarters, the smaller the chance of being kicked.

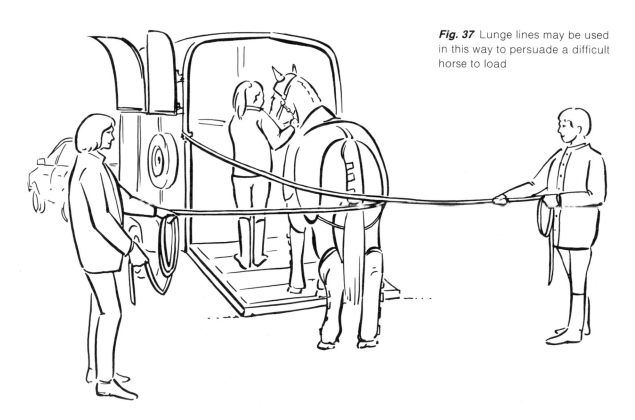

Fig. 37 Lunge lines may be used in this way to persuade a difficult horse to load

Unloading

The vehicle should be parked in a safe and suitable place which allows the horse enough room to come down the ramp straight. The horse should always be untied before any partition, front bar or breeching strap is undone. He should then be led quietly down the ramp – rushing or jumping off the ramp must be discouraged.

Care of the horse when travelling

It is very unnatural for a horse to stand still in an enclosed space for any length of time. How well a fit horse travels will affect his performance, so it is important that good stable management extends to the time spent travelling. The horse should be warm in winter and cool in summer, with adequate fresh air but no draughts, and the floor should be non-slip with minimum noise and disturbance. Most horses will travel well if they are driven carefully in a vehicle with adequate space and good suspension.

Many horse vehicles are inadequately ventilated, particularly in the summer with a full complement of horses on board. In these conditions, horses should wear sweat sheets or thermal clothing to keep them as dry as possible. One horse in a trailer may become quite cold, even on a sunny day, but a through draught can be avoided by travelling with the back top doors closed. This will also prevent the horse from being frightened as lorries overtake the trailer.

22 A horse dressed for travelling. The rugs that he wears will depend on the weather and time of year

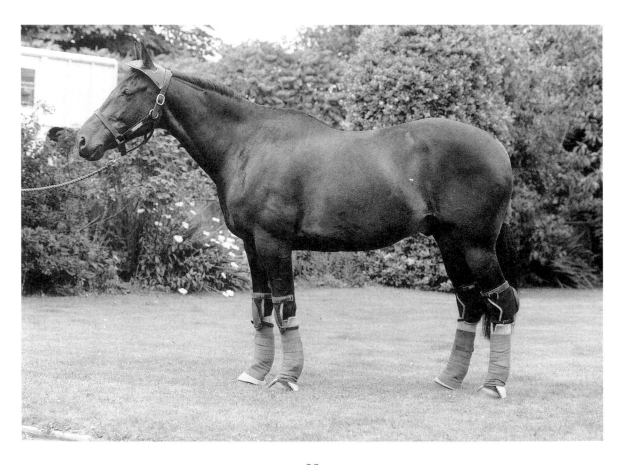

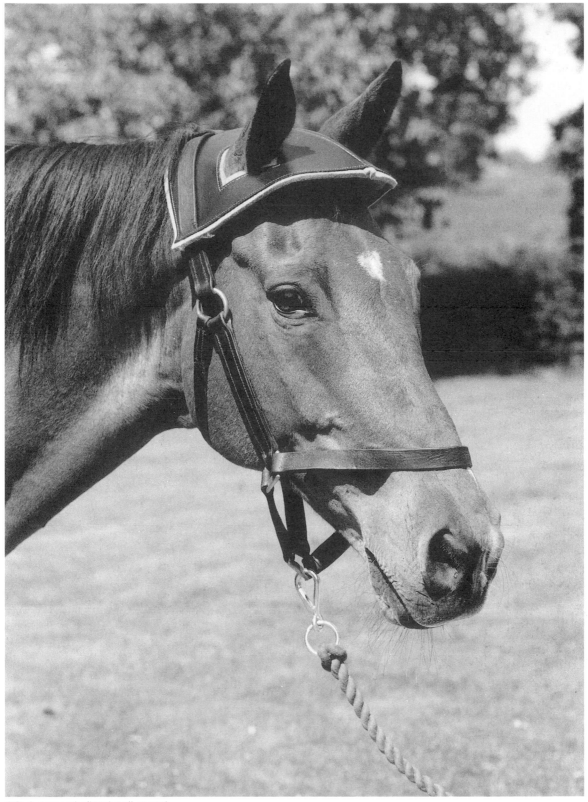

23 A correctly fitted poll guard

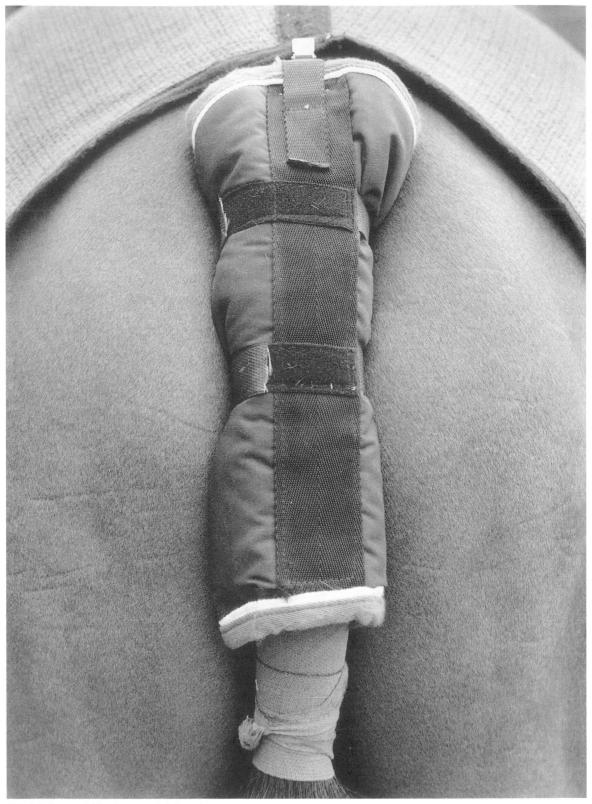

24 A tail guard fitted over a tail bandage

Clothing for travelling

The clothing worn by the horse will depend on the time of year, the weather, the length of the journey, whether he is travelling alone, how well he travels and the type of vehicle: See **(22)** on page 98. The equipment needed includes:

- headcollar (halter), rope and poll guard **(23)**
- sweat rug or thermal travelling rug with surcingle or roller, plus, in winter, the equivalent of his normal day rugs
- travelling boots *or*
- bandages with knee, hock and coronet boots
- tail bandage and tail guard **(24)**
- spare rugs in case the others get wet or the horse sweats up

Feeding on journeys

One of the major problems when travelling long distances is dehydration. It is very important to offer the horse water at frequent intervals – every two hours is ideal. If the horse is sweating, it is wise to include some electrolytes. Some horses are more fussy about water than they are about food, so take water from home in a couple of containers so that the taste of unfamiliar water will not put him off drinking. If this is a real problem, try adding a little molasses to the water at home so that you can do the same at your destination and disguise the different taste. Fortunately, most horses will drink when they are thirsty, no matter what the water tastes like!

The horse will have spent a long time standing still during the journey. As you do not want his legs to fill or for him to experience any other metabolic upsets, this means that the concentrate ration must be cut down, but, on the other hand,

CARE ON LONG JOURNEYS

- On long journeys, the horse should be checked regularly and rugs added or removed as necessary.
- A tail guard is better than a bandage, as a bandage can tighten and rub.
- Regular exercise is essential, and if possible the horse should be walked in hand for at least thirty minutes at every morning and evening stop-over. The horse should wear a simple bridle with a lunge line for control.
- Leg bandages or travelling boots should be taken off twice a day, and the legs rubbed briskly to encourage blood circulation and to prevent filled legs.
- Even with a non-slip floor, there should be enough bedding (straw or shavings) to encourage the horse to stale during the journey.
- After a long journey, a horse is likely to need a day with very quiet exercise to recover, and his work can then be built up gradually to the competition. For this reason, it is important to allow plenty of time before the competition for the journey and the horse's recovery time.

you do not want the fit horse to lose condition. This dilemma is best solved by allowing the horse plenty of good-quality hay during the journey, so that his gut is kept moving and is partially full all the time – this will reduce the risk of colic. The concentrate feeds should be small and easily digested, and given at regular intervals. It may be useful to give the horse a bran mash the evening before the journey and only hay or a very small feed, including bran, the morning before setting off.

On trips taking several days, your vet may recommend that the horse is drenched with mineral oil to prevent impaction colic (see pages 66–7). This can occur in horses which are eating a roughage diet and possibly not getting a full water intake.

7
COMPETITION PROCEDURE

The routine that you follow at a competition will obviously vary depending on the discipline in which you are competing, but there are other factors that will affect the way in which you care for the horse. A local one-day competition will mean that you have to be organized to work from your box or trailer, while a competition spread over several days, or a long way from home, will involve overnight stabling.

One-day competitions

Find out what time your class starts or what your specific start times are, so that you know in advance what time your horse is expected to compete. You can then work backward from this time to calculate when you should arrive at the show ground and therefore what time you must leave home, what time you should start plaiting and doing all the other morning routine tasks, and finally what time you must set your alarm clock so that the horse is fed to allow him to digest his feed before travelling. Food stays in the horse's stomach for about forty-five minutes and it will take him about fifteen minutes to eat his feed, so he must be fed at

least an hour before your expected loading-up time.

Allow time for delays in your journey, and about forty-five minutes to an hour to get yourself organized and the horse settled and tacked up before he needs to be ridden. If you have a cross-country course to walk, give yourself an hour to do this. Horses gallop round in about five minutes, but it takes a lot longer on your own two feet! Allowing time for all these things may involve you in a very early start, and so you may choose to plait up the night before. Bear in mind, however, that a horse will associate being plaited up with competing and may fret in anticipation, and an anxious horse may not compete at his best the following day. There is also a chance that the horse will try to rub out his plaits, ruining his beautifully pulled mane, so it may be worth getting up half an hour earlier to avoid these problems.

On arrival

Park the trailer or horse box where the ground is as level as possible, and, if the weather is warm, try to find some shade. If you have help and the horse has had a long journey, your assistant should unload the horse quietly and walk him in hand until he has relaxed, cooled down and staled. Letting him graze will help to relax him, but make sure that the grass is suitable and has not been contaminated in any way. Meanwhile, you can go and declare for your class, pick up your number and find out where everything is. Even if you are on your own, it is important that the horse stretches his legs, has a look around and is given the chance to urinate, as many horses are reluctant to stale in the vehicle. Make sure that the horse is suitably restrained: some horses may be as good as gold in a headcollar (halter), while others may need to be led in a bridle for extra control.

If the weather is set to be fine and you have a helper who can stay at the vehicle, it is useful to unload the equipment and set it up outside, but if you are on your own or it is raining you will have to work out of the back of the vehicle. This means that you have to be very well-organized, know where everything is and put things back in place as you go along, or there will be chaos with items being mislaid and lost.

Wherever possible, take your own water to a competition. Horses can be very fussy drinkers, and you do not want to run the risk of your horse becoming dehydrated. If you use water at a competition, run it from a tap so that it is fresh, as water from a trough may have been contaminated by other horses.

Unless your horse has been taught to tie up properly and there is no risk of him pulling back, it is wise not to tie him up to the side of your trailer or lorry – this is where a helper is invaluable. If you do have to tie him to the trailer, tie the headcollar (halter) rope to a loop of string placed through the tie-ring, which will break if the horse pulls back violently.

25 A pointed stud fitted on the outside of a hind shoe

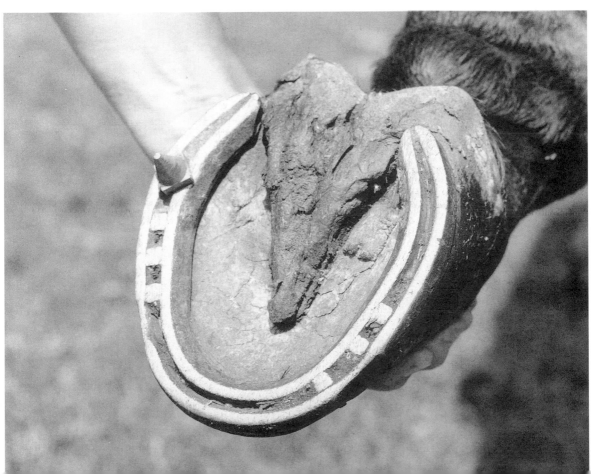

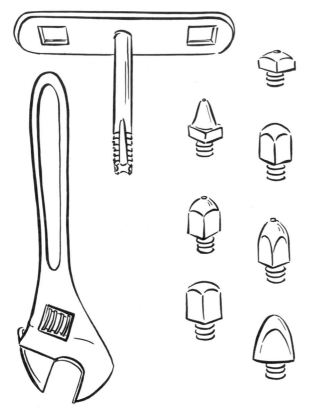

The next step is to brush the horse over. He will have been thoroughly groomed at home, and should only need the finishing touches such as hoof oil, quarter marks and the last obstinate shaving taken out of his tail. If the competition is on grass, the horse may be fitted with studs to give him more grip: see **(25)** on the previous page. The type of stud used will depend on the going, with more pointed studs being used on hard ground and squarer studs on soft ground **(fig. 38)**. Generally, horses can wear studs in the outer quarter of each shoe, although front studs may shorten the stride of a dressage horse.

The horse is now ready to be tacked up. The type of bit that you choose will depend both on the competition in which you are riding, and the controllability of the horse **(figs. 39 to 43)**. For the cross-country phase of a three-day event, good leg protection is of vital importance: see **(26)** to **(31)** on pages 106–11.

Fig. 38 Various types of stud, with a spanner and T-shaped thread cleaner. The smaller, more pointed studs are used on hard ground, and the larger, squarer ones on soft ground

Fig. 39 Mild snaffle bits

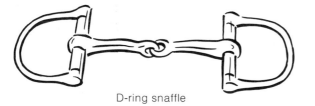

Nylon straight-bar snaffle

Loose-ring jointed snaffle

D-ring snaffle

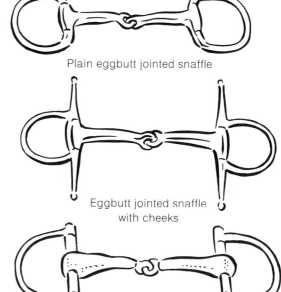

Plain eggbutt jointed snaffle

Eggbutt jointed snaffle with cheeks

Vulcanite D-ring jointed snaffle

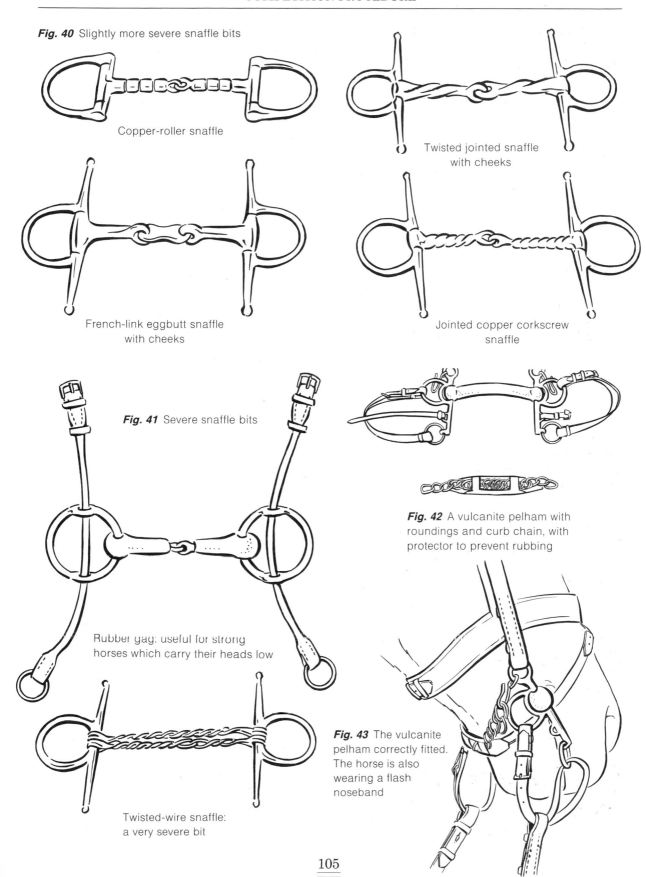

Fig. 40 Slightly more severe snaffle bits

Copper-roller snaffle

Twisted jointed snaffle
with cheeks

French-link eggbutt snaffle
with cheeks

Jointed copper corkscrew
snaffle

Fig. 41 Severe snaffle bits

Rubber gag: useful for strong
horses which carry their heads low

Twisted-wire snaffle:
a very severe bit

Fig. 42 A vulcanite pelham with
roundings and curb chain, with
protector to prevent rubbing

Fig. 43 The vulcanite
pelham correctly fitted.
The horse is also
wearing a flash
noseband

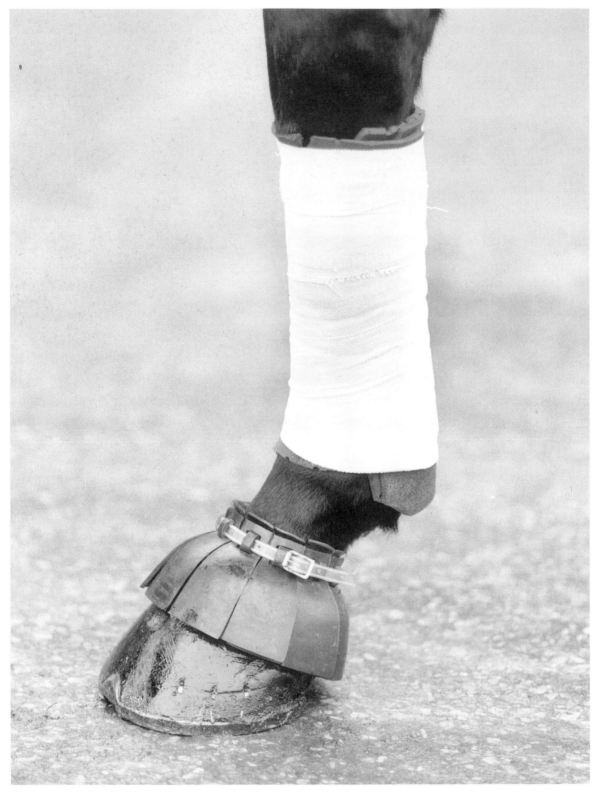

26 Leg protection for a cross-country course. Here, an exercise bandage
is fitted over a tendon protector with a petal over-reach boot

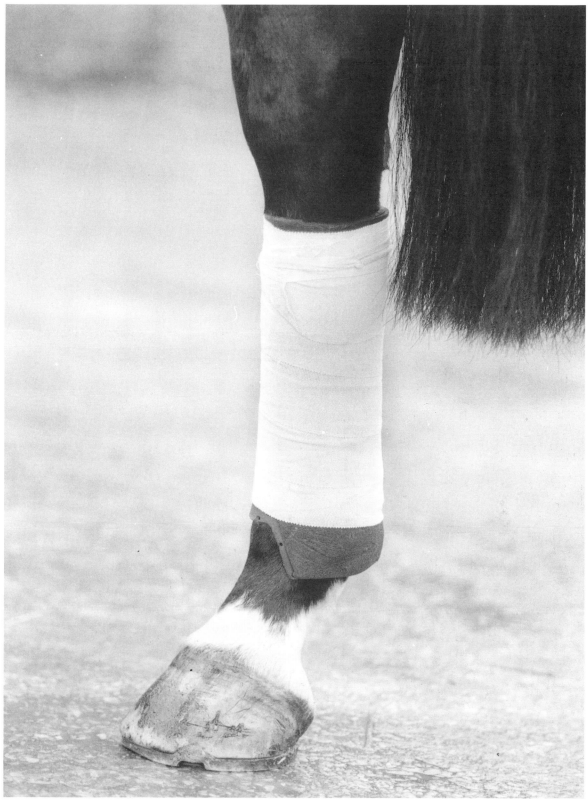

27 A hind leg protected with an exercise bandage and tendon protector

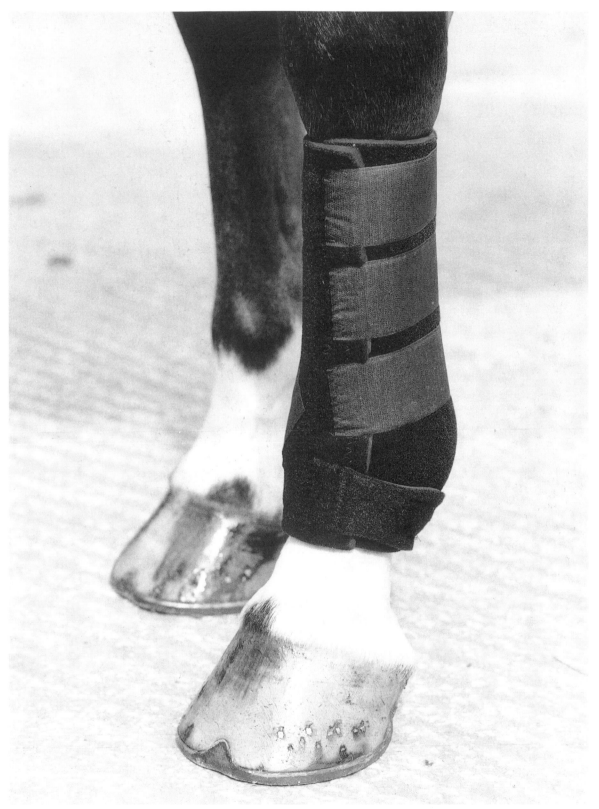

28 A tendon-support boot seen from the outside of the leg

29 A tendon-support boot shown from the inside of the leg.
The boot extends over the fetlock to absorb concussion

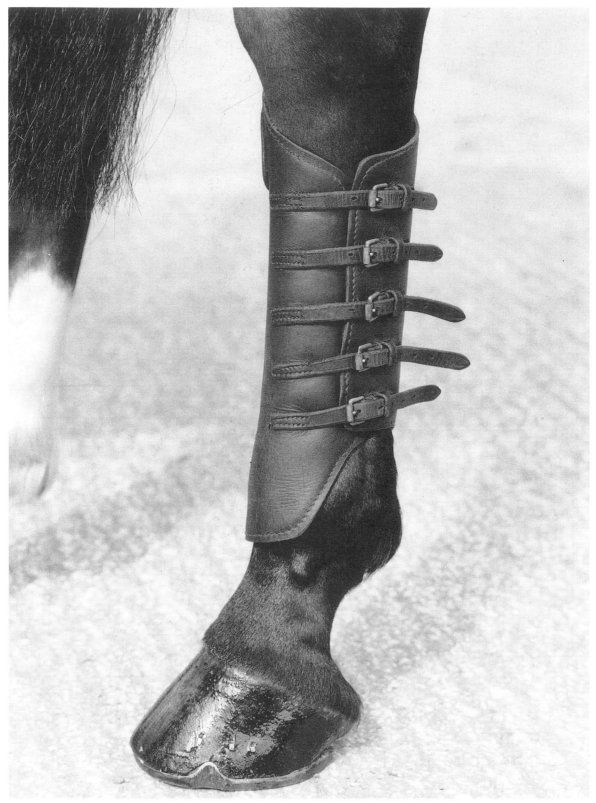

30 A hind leg protected by a leather speedicut boot, seen from the outside of the leg

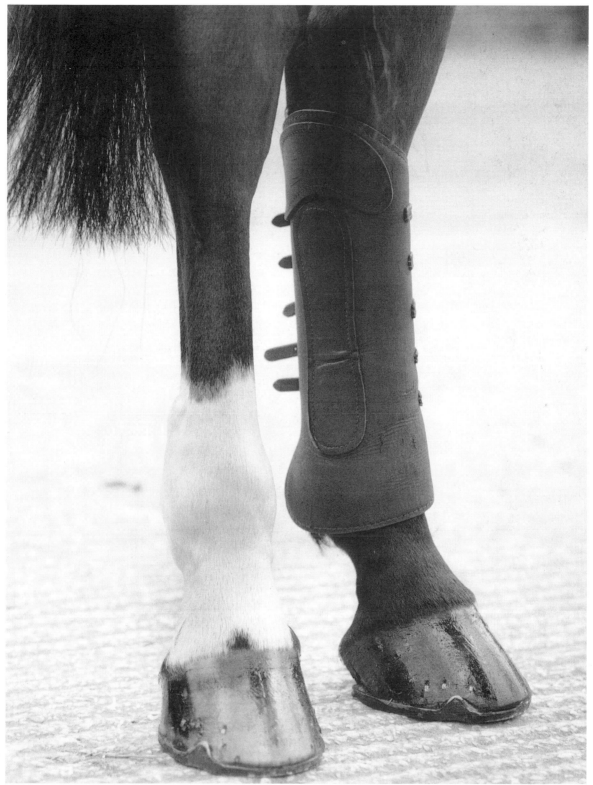

31 A leather speedicut boot shown from the inside. Note that the boot protects the fetlocks and is also padded on the inside of the hock, to protect against brushing wounds sustained when the horse is galloping

Overnight stays

If you are staying overnight at a show ground or racecourse, you will need to have all your horse's vaccination papers up to date and ready to show the officials. At international competitions, your horse's passport will be kept for the duration of the competition, and with it all records of vaccinations and blood tests. A vet will check that the horse is the same as the one on the passport and will perform a basic health check.

CHECKING THE STABLING AT A COMPETITION

- Clean out any old bedding, as this may be contaminated or mouldy.
- Wash out and disinfect the manger.
- Clean out the automatic drinker, if present (you may prefer to turn this off and use buckets if you wish to monitor your horse's water intake).
- Check that the lights work and are out of the horse's reach.
- If there is a drain in the floor, check that the cover is safe.
- Check that glass-covered windows are safe and out of reach.
- Ensure that there are no sharp edges or projections which may cut the horse.
- Check that the door is strong, with secure latches and bolts.
- Check that temporary stalls are strong enough and securely erected.
- If the stall is erected on grass, ensure that it does not contain any harmful plants.
- Temporary stabling will be colder than permanent stabling and there may be a condensation problem, so the horse must be rugged accordingly.
- If cold or wet it may be useful to tie plastic sacks over the open fronts of the stabling to prevent draughts and the horse getting wet.
- Check that the horse cannot touch the horse next door.

Once the horse has been unloaded and had a walk to stretch his legs, he can go into his stable for a roll. After being offered a drink, he will benefit from a small haynet to munch on, so that by the time you offer him a feed he will be relaxed enough to eat it. Depending on the horse, it may be wise to keep thick, protective stable bandages on to prevent him from hurting himself when rolling in a strange stable. Even if your horse does not have a late-night feed he should be checked last thing, as you must see that he has settled in this strange environment and is not too warm or too cold.

You will probably have to use your vehicle as a tack room, so try to park as close to the stable as you can. If the lorry park is too far away, you will have to arrange the equipment that you need immediately around the stable, keeping the rest in the lorry, or there may be a spare stable for you to use. In most cases there will be stable manager, who will tell you where to find the farrier, where you can ride, where and when to collect food and bedding and what time the classes are starting.

It is important to try to keep the horse's routine as much like normal as possible, which includes his feedstuffs and hay, and feed, work and grazing times. This will keep him more relaxed and happy, and the happier he is, the easier your job and the better his performance are likely to be.

Warming up

As the horse begins to work, there is an increase in muscular activity: muscles contract to move the bones to which they are attached, and hence move the horse. Muscles need energy to contract, and initially this energy is supplied by the breakdown of fuels stored within the muscle cells. When these stores run out,

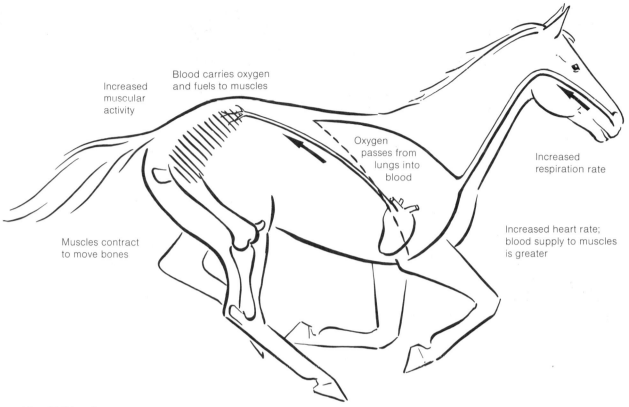

Increased muscular activity

Blood carries oxygen and fuels to muscles

Oxygen passes from lungs into blood

Increased respiration rate

Muscles contract to move bones

Increased heart rate; blood supply to muscles is greater

Fig. 44 Warming up

fuels are supplied from other parts of the body. The liver is a major store of glycogen, which is brought in the bloodstream to the muscle cells in the form of glucose, to be used as an energy source. The horse can also use free fatty acids to produce the energy needed for muscle contraction.

Releasing the energy from these fuels with optimum efficiency requires oxygen, which is taken from the environment by the horse's respiratory system **(fig. 44)**. The horse inhales air deep into the lungs, where the oxygen is extracted, passes into the bloodstream and is transported to the muscle cells by the red blood cells. The oxygen is carried in chemical combination with a substance called haemoglobin, which is contained within the red blood cells. Once in the muscle cells, the oxygen reacts with the fuels to produce energy for muscle contraction. During this process, the waste product carbon dioxide is produced, which must be removed from the cells if the muscles are to continue working. The carbon dioxide is attached to haemoglobin in the blood and taken to the lungs, and is then exhaled.

This means that, not only does the bloodstream supply oxygen and fuels, it also removes waste products. The harder the horse works, the more rapidly his muscles contract and the more oxygen is needed. The heart, which is responsible for pumping blood round the body, must therefore beat faster and more powerfully as the level of exercise increases, in order to push the blood round the body rapidly to supply these demands. The rate and depth of breathing must also increase so that more oxygen is drawn into the body. As we start to warm up our horse, we are immediately aware that both the heart rate and the respiration rate increase. This ensures both an increased supply of oxygen to the muscle cells, and the speedy removal of waste products from the horse's body.

As exercise levels increase, the adrenal glands release the hormone adrenalin, which promotes a 'fight or flight' reaction in the horse. Breathing and heart rates increase and body fuels are released from their storage depots, priming the body for work. In addition, the horse's spleen (a blood-storage organ) contracts, releasing large numbers of red blood cells into the circulation to increase the oxygen-carrying capacity of the blood, enabling further muscle contraction. The horse is now said to be working *aerobically*.

During very strenuous exercise, the horse's muscles will be working at maximum capacity and will have a very high oxygen demand. Sometimes the oxygen demands of the muscles will exceed the amount of oxygen that can be supplied by the blood – the horse has a maximum respiration rate and there is a limit to how fast the heart can beat, so there is a maximum oxygen uptake. When the energy demands of the muscles are greater than can be supplied by burning the body fuels in the presence of oxygen, the body finds an alternative to top up the energy levels. This extra energy for muscle contraction is obtained from the fuel supplies *anaerobically* – in other words, in the absence of oxygen.

The anaerobic production of energy is less efficient than producing energy aerobically, and is really a source of short-term power at the expense of limited fuel resources. In addition, a potentially poisonous waste product called lactic acid is produced, which is considered to be a major contributor to muscle fatigue. High levels of lactic acid are associated with muscle cramps, tying-up and muscle damage. The more anaerobic work a horse has to perform, the more energy he will use up and the quicker he will tire.

Lactic acid is taken by the blood to the liver, where it is detoxified, but oxygen is needed to do this and so the process can only take place at the end of anaerobic exercise, when the horse pulls up or slows down. This is one of the reasons why a horse blows at the end of exercise. The longer he has worked anaerobically, the longer he will blow and the slower his recovery time will be as he 'repays the oxygen debt'. At slower levels of exercise, the oxygen supply can keep up with oxygen demand and lactic acid does not accumulate.

Warming up the horse must prepare him mentally for the task that he is about to perform, be it jumping or dressage, and must also prime the body systems so that they are able to work as efficiently as possible.

Effective warming up

Human athletes are meticulous with their warming-up exercises, because they are only too aware that, unless the body systems are correctly primed before work, the inevitable result is at best poor performance and at worst strains and sprains. The competition horse should be treated in the same way; the dressage horse, for example, should not be expected to perform collected movements as soon as he comes out of the stable. You like to have a stretch and a few minutes to loosen up when you get out of bed, not go straight into press-ups!

The type and degree of warm-up will obviously depend on the discipline, and is most important for the horse that is expected to produce speed. Whatever discipline you are warming up for, the horse should have fifteen minutes of loosening and suppling work in walk and trot before he is asked to do any serious work. The horse may be very tense when you first get on him, and, as tense muscles do not allow the blood to enter and leave them freely, this means that vital nutrients cannot get into the muscles. As a result, when the horse is asked to work harder, the muscles will work anaerobically, with consequent lactic-acid build-up.

Racehorses are warmed up thoroughly. Initially, they are walked round the paddock for as long as twenty minutes before they are cantered down to the start, where they catch their breath while the girths are checked, and are then ready to go. Similarly, the three-day-event horse is thoroughly warmed up by the roads and tracks of Phase A before the steeplechase, and then has time to recover in the ten-minute box before the start of the cross-country. The one-day-event horse, the hunter-trial horse and the team chaser are less likely to be so well-prepared, however, and the rider must be aware of this. The horse should have ten minutes' walk and trot, a three-minute canter and a three-minute walk. If the start is delayed after this, a short canter immediately before starting will be sufficient.

The amount of warming up that a horse will need prior to a dressage test will vary on the degree of training of the horse and his mental attitude to work. You are not just priming the body systems you are also preparing the horse mentally, he has to be accurate and obedient in the arena. Generally all horses should be prepared to start work after ten to fifteen minutes of suppling work, with a further fifteen minutes of fine tuning before the test. It is a mistake to get the event horse into the habit of needing longer and longer periods of warming up. He may be very tense; he is fit to run cross country and he knows perfectly well that galloping and jumping follow the dressage. Rather than work the horse for an hour before his test which may make him bored and the resulting test flat, try working him for half an hour when

THE IMPORTANCE OF CORRECT WARMING UP

- Warming up ensures that sufficient blood is diverted from the horse's core to the muscles that are going to be involved in locomotion. An inadequate blood supply results in a shortage of nutrients for the contracting muscles, leading to premature fatigue and the chance of subsequent injury.
- Warming up may require special attention to specific areas. Human athletes massage calf and thigh muscles prior to exercise, and your horse may need the same type of attention.
- Effective warming up primes the body systems and is essential for efficient performance and for minimising the stress on the body during exertion.
- Warming up also prepares the horse mentally for the task he is about to perform.

you arrive, putting him back in the box and then doing another 30 minutes before the test. The tense horse may also benefit by going to dressage competitions which are generally less crowded and exciting and have the advantage of not having a jump in sight!

The one day event horse will have already performed a dressage test before his show jumping and thus tends to need only five or ten minutes of loosening up before going over a practice fence. Do not jump too many practice fences or you may "leave the horses jump in the collecting ring".

8
COMPETING

The successful competitor is not one who wins at the expense of his horse, but one who is able to get the best performance out of the horse, depending on the horse's ability and the conditions on the day. A horse that is pushed to the limit due to thoughtless or selfish riding may lose his spirit, while a horse that is brought on carefully will grow in confidence and give of his best.

The care of a horse that is enduring strenuous competition is vital to success on the day and to how well the horse recovers from the work. The recovery aspect is vital for both the endurance horse and the three-day-event horse, as the endurance horse has to pass a stringent veterinary test soon after completing a ride, and the eventer has to pass a vet check before being allowing to compete in the final day's show jumping. This chapter takes a look at aspects of the care of these horses during their competition.

Endurance riding

Entries usually close at least a week before the event so that competitors can be sent a copy of the route and instructions. It is worth transferring the route on to a coloured map, which will be much easier to follow than a photocopy when you are riding. If you receive a written route description with the map, read it carefully to familiarize yourself with the route before the ride. There will be a number of checkpoints on the ride that you must go through in the correct direction. You need to work out at what time you should arrive at each checkpoint, so that you can keep a check on your speed during the ride.

On the day

On the day of the ride, plan to arrive at least thirty minutes before your veterinary check time, and report to the secretary to collect your number and to check whether there are any last-minute route changes or instructions. Once you have unloaded your horse and walked off any stiffness he may be feeling after the journey, report to the veterinary steward a few minutes before the time for your vet check. If you have a helper with you, ask them to remove any rugs that your horse may have on as the vet requires. The horse should be wearing a bridle, so that you have more control if he becomes excited. The vet will check his pulse, ask you to trot him up to ensure that he is sound, and will look for

32 The attendance of the back-up team is crucial to the endurance horse's performance *(Kit Houghton Photography)*

any lumps and bumps. If you know that your horse has any cuts or lumps, make sure that they are noted on the veterinary card before you start the ride.

Once your horse has passed the vet check, you will have a short time to tack up and get ready. There will be a tack inspection just before you start. At the beginning of the ride, try to keep to a sensible speed until the horse is fully warmed up, or you may find that he starts tying-up. When he is warmed up it is advisable to ride the first part of the route faster than is required, to give yourself some time in hand for any unforeseen problems.

Getting lost on a ride is an occupational hazard, so keep checking your position on the map while you are riding. Most routes run along public rights of way, so be courteous to other users and also to checkpoint stewards, and make sure that they have time to note your number before you ride on.

Your helper(s) should meet you at pre-arranged points on the route, so that even if your horse does not want to drink he can be sponged down: see (32) on the previous page. It is important for the horse to learn to drink during rides, so let him stop at streams and troughs, although many horses will not drink for about twenty miles unless it is a very hot day.

The shorter rides of up to thirty miles do not have a halfway halt for vetting, and when you finish the ride you will have thirty minutes from your finish time to your final vetting. Immediately after finishing, loosen your horse's girth, but do not take off the saddle straight away as the cold air hitting the hot back can cause a scalded back or pressure lumps to appear. The horse will need cooling to bring his pulse down. Check his pulse with a steth-oscope and, if it is a lot higher than the allowed 64 beats per minute, sponge him with plenty of water, particularly on his neck and chest and between the hind legs, where the large blood vessels pass close to the skin. Do not get cold water on the large muscles of the back and top of the quarters, as this will make him stiffen up. Check the pulse frequently to see how quickly it is dropping: the fitter the horse, the faster his pulse will fall.

Once the horse is washed down, throw a rug over his quarters, remove the saddle and rub the area with a towel to encourage the circulation (fig. 45). Let the horse walk around and graze a little, and keep offering him water. Just before you are due to report to the veterinary steward, stop the horse eating, as this puts his pulse up. The vet will carry out the Ridgeway test, which involves taking the horse's pulse, asking you to trot the horse to a marker thirty metres away and back, and then checking the pulse exactly one minute after the first reading. If the horse is sufficiently fit, the second reading will be the same or less than the first, but if the horse is tired, the pulse will go up. The second reading is used as the criterion for penalties or elimination. The vet will also make sure that the horse has no cuts or sores which would make him 'not fit to continue'. Once the vetting is over, you can relax.

It is advisable to compete in a few shorter-distance rides over different terrain before rushing into the longer rides, although a twenty-mile ride in rough, hilly country can be a lot tougher than a longer ride on flat, soft tracks. Once you feel ready to do a forty-mile ride, the only difference in procedure is that there is a halfway halt for a vet check. This is a thirty-minute halt with the vet check after twenty minutes, at which the Ridgeway test is used, as at the final vetting.

Endurance riders need to be familiar with their horse and expert in monitoring the degree of exertion and the speed of the recovery.

Fig. 45 Rubbing the saddle area with a towel encourages circulation after a long ride. A rug over the horse's quarters will keep him warm

Care of your horse

Endurance riders use a lot of water on their horses, encouraging them to drink whenever they wish and literally throwing water over them on hot days. When horses are offered water throughout the ride, they usually drink little and often: see **(33)** overleaf. It is unusual for anyone to have a problem through letting their horses drink too much, but there have been cases where horses have become seriously dehydrated. Electrolytes are very important to endurance horses, and can be given in the feed for a day or two before the ride, and during the ride in water or sugar-beet liquid. They are sometimes given by syringing concentrated electrolyte solution into the horse's mouth during a ride, but this must never be done before the horse has started to drink well, or it will cause fluid to be drawn into the stomach from the tissues and further dehydrate the horse. If a horse is not drinking sufficiently, it does help to pour water over his neck.

As you compete in longer and faster rides, the care of the horse during and after the ride becomes increasingly critical. The technique of getting through vet gates on race rides can win or lose a race. Race rides are all run under similar rules, and cover between fifty and a hundred miles in a day. The first horse to finish and pass the final veterinary inspection is the winner. It is not unusual for the first horse to fail the vetting, especially if there is a racing finish, so winning a race ride is not just about speed.

In the course of the ride, there are vet gates at approximately twenty-five-mile intervals, where the horses are examined

by a vet panel, and any judged unfit to continue are eliminated. You are timed into the vet gate and have a maximum time of thirty minutes to present your horse for vetting. Once your horse has passed the vet with a pulse of 64 b.p.m. or lower, there is a timed 'hold', which can be from ten minutes to one hour depending on the length of the ride and weather conditions, before you can leave the vet gate. If the horse fails the vet on his pulse rate the first time you present him for vetting, you may re-present him after a minimum of ten minutes, as long as you have not been in the vet gate for more than thirty minutes. Lameness incurs elimination.

The aim is to get through the vet gates as quickly as possible, as the time from entering the vet gate, up to when you request the inspection, is all part of the total riding time. The experienced horse-and-rider combinations usually present for inspection within five minutes of arriving at the vet gate.

There is a marker 1 km ($\frac{5}{8}$ mile) from the vet gate, warning riders of their approach to it. The back-up crew and rider may not attend to the horse in this last section. The rider should aim to come into the vet gate slowly, so that the horse's pulse will drop rapidly or will already be below 64 b.p.m. An experienced competitor will present their horse for vetting as soon as the pulse is at 60 b.p.m., which does not give much room for error! Less-experienced riders and crews should wait an extra minute or two to be sure that the pulse is continuing to fall, as it only takes another horse arriving at the gate to put the pulse up by a few beats per minute.

By the time the rider comes into the vet gate, the back-up crew should be waiting with all the necessary equipment: water containers, stethoscope, buckets, sponges, towels, clean numnahs (saddle pads) and girths, feed if required and also food and drink for the rider. As soon as the horse is timed in, his pulse should be checked. If it is above 64 b.p.m., the horse must be cooled down quickly: wash him down with plenty of water and offer him a drink. Stand him in the shade if possible, but do remember that his pulse will go up again once he is brought out into the sun for vetting. Damp towels or towelling rugs can be left on until the pulse has been taken, if the vet does not object. If it is a cold day, confine water to the large veins on the neck and chest and between the hind legs, and keep a rug over the horse's quarters to stop him stiffening up. Once the pulse has dropped to below 64 b.p.m., wait for a minute and check that it is still dropping before asking the vet steward to direct you to one of the vets. If the pulse does not seem to be dropping steadily, wait rather than risk the vet finding it to be over 64 b.p.m. and making you wait for ten minutes to re-present.

Once through the vet check, the horse should be allowed to graze and have a drink if he wishes. Many horses do not start drinking for 30–40 km (20–30 miles), but once they start, they usually drink well during the rest of the ride. If the weather is hot, the horse may need further cooling. Some riders feed their horses during a ride, but do not give too much, as digestion puts an additional strain on the horse's system. While the back-up crew tends to the horse, the rider should get some refreshment and rest. By the end of the ride, the horse may be fine, but you will be in a state of exhaustion!

As the race proceeds, the back-up crew needs to meet the horse as often as possible, especially on a hot day. This takes careful planning and can involve a very high mileage, and the crew must allow plenty of time to get from point to point as

33 Drinking during the ride is important, and the horse should be allowed to stop at water when it is encountered on the ride *(Kit Houghton Photography)*

the roads are usually busy with other back-up cars. Prompt arrival at the vet gates to set everything up and meet the rider is essential. 'Slosh' bottles – 4–5 litre (8–10 pint) containers – are filled with water and handed to the rider as he rides past, and are used to pour over the horse to cool him.

The last gate is usually situated about ten miles from the finish. Once successfully through this vet gate, you can push on as fast as you feel your horse is able, as you will have thirty minutes after the finish to get the pulse down before the final vetting. Make sure that there is plenty of water available at the end of the

ride for cooling the horse. There is usually a water supply at the venue.

Your first gated ride can be an exhausting competition, especially as these rides all have mass starts. Decide whether to go in front with the faster horses, or to try to settle your horse at a steadier pace near the back. Avoid being 'towed' by the front-runners too fast for your horse's good, as he will eventually run out of steam. Once through the first vet gate, the horses spread out and it is easier to set your own speed. You may be riding on your own for long periods. Most horses learn quickly and, once they have done one or two longer rides, will steady themselves.

Fig. 46 Dressage day at a three-day event

Fig. 47 The steeplechase (phase B) of a three-day event

Three-day eventing

The three-day event is considered by many to be the ultimate test for horse and rider, testing skill in dressage, cross-country and show jumping as well as the horse's stamina and bravery. The first day consists of dressage, which demonstrates the horse's obedience and suppleness and the rider's ability to ride correctly and accurately **(fig. 46)**. In large events, the dressage may be spread over two days. The second day is the speed and endurance day, and has four phases – phase A: roads and tracks; phase B: steeplechase **(fig. 47)**; phase C: roads and tracks; and Phase D: cross-country **(see fig. 48 overleaf)**. The final day is a show-jumping test, to prove that the horse is fit, keen and obedient after the previous day's exertions **(fig. 49)**.

The horse undergoes veterinary checks on arrival, the day before the dressage and on the morning of the show jumping **(fig. 50)**. On speed and endurance day, teamwork and the care that the horse receives are vital to his success and well-being. The groom can attend to the horse briefly in the neutral zone after the end of the steeplechase and at the beginning of the second roads and tracks. If the weather is hot, the horse can be sponged down quickly and the shoes checked (there is usually a farrier available). The second place where the horse receives important attention is the ten-minute box. The three-day event groom must be familiar with the four phases of speed and endurance day; the routine, the equipment, where the horse is going to be and how to get to them. It is unlikely that one person can do all this and a team of three is better.

Fig. 48 Successful cross-country riding demands balance, so that the horse can get on with his job and make a good shape over the fence

The ten-minute box

Before starting out on the cross-country, a three-day-event horse has completed about nine miles of roads and tracks and galloped round a steeplechase track for three or four minutes. There is then a ten-minute compulsory halt before the start of the cross-country phase to allow the horse to recover from his exertions. This ten-minute halt, more commonly known as 'the box', plays an important part in determining how well the horse copes with the cross-country, how quickly he recovers for the next day's veterinary inspection, and how he performs in the final day's show-jumping phase.

The team must be organised and well briefed – it is no good everybody trying to do the same jobs.

Equipment

It is vital to be organized when the horse arrives in the box. All the equipment (see page 93) should be laid out in a suitable place: if the weather is hot, choose a shady spot; if it is cold, pick an area sheltered from the wind. Remember too that there will be other horses in the box, so try to stay out of harm's way. Water is likely to be available but will not be suitable for drinking, so take your own to wash out the horse's mouth.

Ice may be supplied in hot conditions, and a farrier should be at hand. If the weather is cold, it is a good idea to have warm water for washing down, so an insulated water carrier is useful. If you do not have one, fill your water containers with really hot water just before you take the equipment to the box.

Soundness

During this halt, the horse undergoes an inspection by a panel of experts, one of whom is a vet. Any horse considered unfit is forbidden to continue to the cross-country phase and withdrawn from the rest of the competition. The horse and rider are required to trot the last twenty-five metres of phase C (roads and tracks), into the box, so that the panel can assess the soundness of the horse. This is also a chance for the groom to observe the horse: apathy and a loss of power in the stride are the first indicators of fatigue and possible tying-up. If necessary, a second trot-up by the groom five minutes later will help to confirm any suspected problems.

Recovery

It is common practice for the vet to take the pulse of every horse once the rider has dismounted. Depending on the conditions on the day, the vet will have decided on an acceptable 'normal' range of pulse rates. Any horse with a pulse rate above this norm will be monitored during the ten-minute halt, and only allowed to continue if the pulse rate drops to an acceptable level before the start of the cross-country. At top three-day events, normal ranges are usually between 100 and 150 beats per minute, and are expected to drop by 20 to 30 beats in the first five minutes. While the vet is taking the horse's pulse, the groom should loosen the horse's girths and nose-band, as this will relieve the horse of any pressure and help him to relax.

Heatstroke and dehydration

As already discussed, the competition horse working in hot and humid conditions is vulnerable to heatstroke and dehydration. The groom's aims must therefore be to:

- assist heat loss from the skin's surface
- lower the heart and respiration rates
- keep blood flowing to the muscles so that the horse remains ready for work
- prepare the horse for the cross-country phase

Fig. 49 The final show-jumping phase tests the horse's recovery from the gruelling cross country

Cooling the horse

The groom's first task is to help the horse to lose heat. At rectal temperatures of 42–3°C (108–9°F) muscle cells within the horse will start to die, and any horse with a rectal temperature of 41°C (106°F) should not be allowed to start the cross-country. As it is not uncommon for horses to finish phase C with rectal temperatures of 39–40°C, (102–4°F), you can see that the margin between a horse being able to continue or not is very slim, especially in hot weather.

Fig. 50 Trotting a horse up for a veterinary panel. Note that the horse is allowed freedom of the head and neck

The main problem in the box is that dramatic cooling methods will decrease the blood volume flowing to the muscles, but it is important for this blood supply to remain high so that the horse stays warmed-up for the cross-country. It is also important to pay off the oxygen debt and prevent the accumulation of lactic acid. The worst thing to do in the box is to apply very cold water or ice to the horse's skin and to stand him still for too long. Reduction of blood to the muscles and skin at this stage will lead to lactic-acid build-up and the possibility of the horse tying up; in order to avoid this, most people do not attempt to cool the muscles of the back, loins and quarters at all.

The most efficient way of reducing the core temperature is to wash the horse's neck, chest, belly and between the hind legs. If the weather is cold, this should be followed by scraping and towel-rubbing to encourage blood back into the peripheral vessels, to prevent the horse from catching a chill. Once rubbed down, the horse should be walked around with a rug on to ensure that he keeps warm. In hot weather, the horse should have copious amounts of water sponged over these areas as he walks around: this will replace sweating and can save the horse as much as half a gallon of sweat during the ten minutes. Walking the horse in shady areas and using electric fans will also assist heat loss. The skin temperature should be assessed regularly to ensure that the horse does not feel cold.

Some people now use ice packs in the box when the weather is very hot. If used, ice must always be wrapped in a cloth, and either applied for a few seconds to one area or kept moving over a large area. It should only be used in areas where there are major blood vessels, such as the throat and between the hind legs – the poll is often used, but serves little purpose as there are no large blood vessels in this area.

Wet towels can be draped over the neck and quarters in an attempt to keep the horse cool. To be effective, these must be changed as soon as they become warm – often every few seconds – or all they will do is prevent heat loss from the area that they cover.

Water provision

Although dehydration is a problem, the horse should not be offered a drink in the box, but a quick, refreshing wash of the mouth can be given. During work, the muscles' demand for oxygen means that the blood vessels of the stomach and gut constrict to divert their blood to the muscles. A drink of cold water will 'shock' the system, depriving the muscles of their vital blood supply and possibly initiating colic.

Respiration rate

In normal weather conditions, the respiration rate will be below that of the pulse, and will fall as the pulse rate falls. In hot, humid conditions, however, although the horse may come back into the box breathing deeply, his breaths will become shallow and more frequent as he recovers. The horse starts to 'pant' in this way in an attempt to cool himself once the oxygen debt has been paid off. As long as the pulse has dropped, the body temperature is below 40°C (104°F) and the other signs of recovery are progressing well, there is no need to worry – just keep the horse moving and continue sponging water over him. If the horse starts panting when he has a high body temperature and rapid pulse, however, he is severely fatigued and near the point of collapse. A horse in this state should not be allowed to continue and should be cooled by continuous hosing, ice packs and fans under veterinary supervision.

Box routine

For the horse the box is a mental break, so the box routine needs to be well-organized and carried out with the minimum fuss. This is the time to check shoes and studs, boots, bandages and the rest of the equipment, and to attend to any problems (see **34** to **40** on pages 128–35). Of the ten minutes, the horse should be kept moving for a minimum of five minutes. Time must also be allowed for re-adjusting and tightening tack, as well as for greasing the horse's legs.

Ideally, the rider should get on the horse three minutes before the start of phase D, so that the horse can be trotted to ensure that he is fully warmed up and has not stiffened up. All that is then left for the groom to do is to wish the rider good luck, re-pack the equipment and prepare to receive the horse at the end of the cross-country, knowing that everything possible has been done to ensure that the horse has a good round.

EQUIPMENT FOR THE BOX

- Waterproof sheet.
- Headcollar (halter) and rope.
- Three buckets and two sponges.
- Sponge for washing out the mouth.
- Sweat scraper and towels.
- Sweat sheet and/or cooler.
- Surcingle.
- Grease and rubber gloves.
- Spare shoes, stud kit and hoof pick.
- Spare boots, bandages, bridle and reins, overgirth, girth, leathers and stirrups, and numnah (saddle pad).
- Small first-aid kit and scissors.
- Hole punch.
- Repair kit: tape, safety pins, elastic bands, needle and thread.
- For the rider: coat, drink, dry gloves, spare whip and spurs, and programme with map of the course.

34 The ten-minute box at Badminton Three-Day Event

35 The horse's mouth is washed out and his nostrils wiped clean

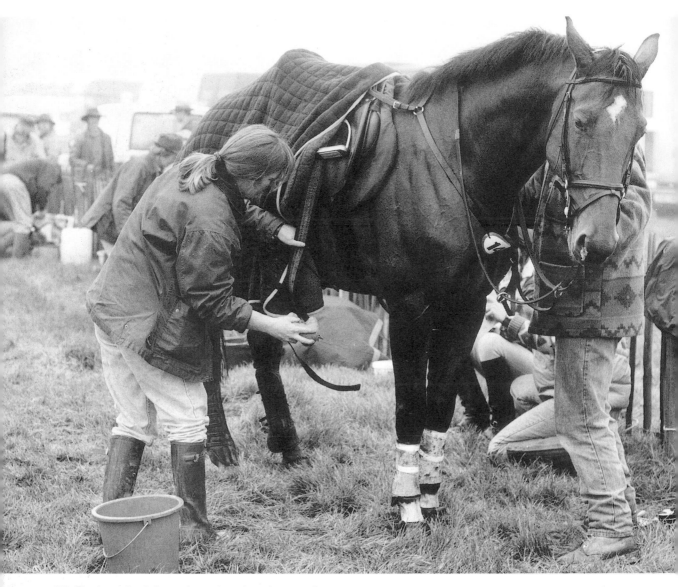

36 The horse's girths and noseband are loosened, and he is sponged to cool him down

37 *(Opposite)* Grease is liberally applied to the front of all four legs to help the horse slide rather than fall over a fence if he hits it hard

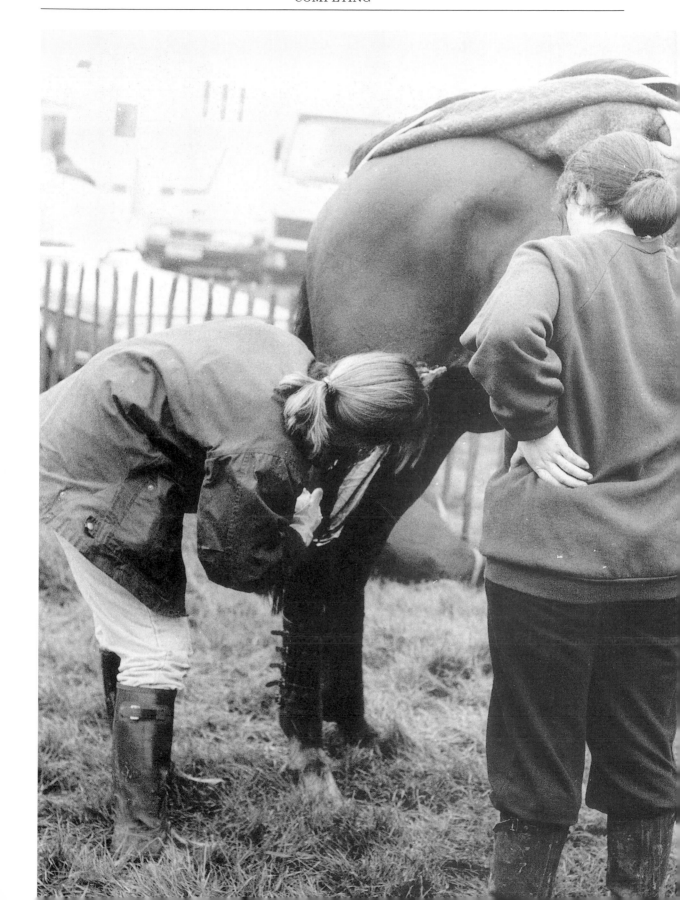

38 While the horse is being tended, the rider and trainer recap on the riding plan

39 Three minutes before the start, the rider is legged up and the girths tightened

40 *(Opposite)* Last-minute instructions, with the horse and rider refreshed and ready to start

Part 3

CARE OF THE HORSE AFTER COMPETITION

9
COOLING DOWN

Horses are often required to work in hot and humid conditions that are severe enough to cause concern for their welfare. The problem has been highlighted in recent years, and eventers and show jumpers could well learn some lessons from long-distance riders, who have learned from experience how to care for their horses under these conditions.

Avoiding heatstroke and dehydration

The horse should be the right type for the job: many long-distance horses are of Arab breeding and may stand only 15 hands high. The three-day-event horse tends to be thoroughbred or seven-eighths thoroughbred, and of lean, athletic build with a flowing, economic action.

The preparation of the horse before the competition must be adequate. The onset of dehydration can be insidious – brought about, for example, by standing in a hot vehicle for several hours. A fit horse should be offered water every hour, particularly if he has worked first. Take care that the horse drinks the water he is offered during his stay at a competition – this may mean bringing water from home

if he is a fussy drinker. If the climate is very hot and the horse is not accustomed to the heat, he may sweat in the stable and start to dehydrate. The stable can be cooled by spraying water on the roof and having fans at the door to create a breeze.

The management of the horse before and during competition is very important. The eventer on cross-country day should have water freely available until an hour or so before the start of phase A, as, if a horse has free access to fresh water, he is unlikely suddenly to drink too much at once. Try to avoid hurrying your horse into the box at the end of phase C, as he will have more recovering to do and the halt will lose much of its value. It is best to walk the last hundred metres or so, remembering to trot the last twenty-five metres for the inspection panel. The care of the horse in the box has been discussed fully on pages 95–101.

The long-distance horse must have water freely available before the ride, and should be encouraged to drink every time you encounter water to prevent him from becoming excessively thirsty during the ride. The route of the ride may make it impossible to keep the horse so well-watered that he arrives at each drinking place in a fit state to drink all the water he wishes without pause. Indeed, many horses will not drink until they have completed twenty to thirty miles. In these cases, the horse should stay by the water, drinking at intervals until his thirst is quenched. If he is not satisfied at this stage, he will only be even more thirsty at the next watering place. Drinks of fifteen to twenty swallows (two litres [4·2 pints]) followed by a pause of one minute are advised. The horse should then be walked for several hundred yards until the water in the stomach has had time to warm up.

Electrolytes

Electrolytes are powders or liquids given in the water or feed before, during and after competition, to replace electrolytes lost during sweating. After a competition it may take five or six days to replace the potassium lost during heavy sweating. A potassium deficiency is known to be a factor in the human equivalent of azoturia (see pages 67–68), and may contribute to horses tying up after strenuous exercise. The best plan is to use electrolytes for a couple of days before, during and after major stress in warm, humid conditions. Horses sweat at home as well, so electrolytes should be used after fast work or schooling if the horse has sweated heavily.

Electrolytes are an essential part of an endurance horse's diet. The horse cannot store electrolytes to any appreciable extent, but adding them to his feed or water a day or two prior to the event can help. During the ride, the ideal way to give electrolytes is in water, but the horse must be accustomed to this – do not stop him drinking by adding electrolytes, as this obviously defeats the object of the exercise. Alternatively, electrolytes can be added to watery sugar-beet pulp. A concentrated electrolyte solution can be syringed down the horse's throat, but this must never be done until he has started drinking, as it can cause further dehydration by drawing water from the tissues into the stomach. Electrolytes are needed on longer rides in hot weather, but there is a tendency to over-use them. In many situations, use before and after the ride is sufficient.

Care after the competition

After finishing an arduous competition, the horse will benefit from thoughtful and efficient treatment. He will have a high temperature and his pulse and respiration rates will also be up, and it is important to get these body systems back to normal as quickly as possible.

Walking the horse

Immediately the horse has stopped, the rider should dismount and loosen the girth. Unless you have to weigh in, this is not the time to untack – it is more important to keep the horse moving so that the circulating blood will cool the muscles, carrying away heat and lactic acid. If the horse is kept standing, blood will pool in the muscles, 'trapping' lactic acid and causing stiffness, and perhaps inducing tying-up or colic. After five minutes' walking, the tack can be removed, a cooler or sweat rug put on and walking continued (see **41** overleaf). If the saddle has been on for a long time, it should be left in place for about ten minutes to allow circulation in the blood vessels to return; sudden removal can cause a scalded back and pressure lumps.

Checking temperature, pulse and respiration

The temperature, pulse and respiration rates should be taken, to see how much above normal they are, and to monitor

41 Once the rider has been congratulated, the horse must be kept walking until his pulse and respiration rates have returned to comfortable levels

how quickly they fall. This will indicate how stressed the horse has been and how well he is recovering. The pulse and respiration rates of a fit horse which has not been over-stressed should return to comfortable levels within fifteen minutes. The horse should be checked every fifteen minutes thereafter until the values return to normal, which should be within an hour of completing exercise. Speedy recovery is important if the horse is to be able to jump clear the next day.

Washing down

Once the pulse and respiration are within comfortable levels, the horse should be stood in a sheltered place, out of the sun on a hot day and out of the wind on a cool day, and washed down **(42)**. If the horse's temperature is no more than 41°C (106°F), tepid water can be used to cool him. Water that is too cold will cause the peripheral blood vessels to constrict so that heat is unable to escape from the muscles to the

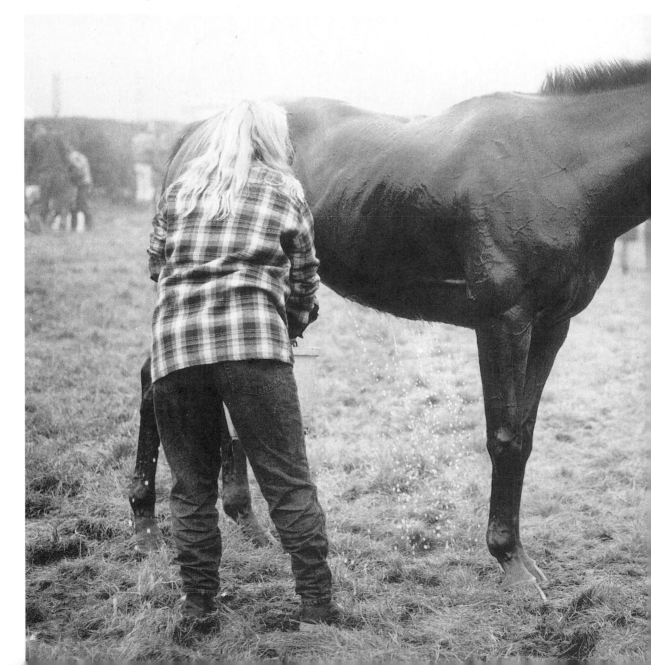

surface, and this will hinder cooling. The lower legs, inside the legs, the head and the belly should be sponged, but the large muscle masses of the back and quarters must be avoided as sudden cooling can send them into spasm.

If the horse's temperature is over 41°C (106°F) and the weather is hot and humid, the horse must be cooled as quickly as possible and the vet called. Ice packs can be used where major blood vessels pass close to thin skin: for example, between the hind legs, under the tail and the jowl. If the muscles are shaking from stress, the horse should be kept moving, with one person leading and another sponging the horse.

Fig. 51 Offer the horse a few swallows of water while he is walking

Water provision

Once the horse's temperature has dropped to below 40°C (104°F) and the pulse and respiration are within comfortable limits, the horse can have some water **(fig. 51)**. When a horse is exercising, adrenalin stimulates contraction of the blood vessels in the gut so that blood can be diverted to the muscles. While the horse is cooling down, blood must be kept in the muscles, but, if he drinks, blood will be diverted away from the muscles to the gut. The horse will therefore not cool down

42 The horse is then washed down and should be kept moving once the excess water has been scraped off. In cold weather his loins and quarters should be kept covered

efficiently and may even colic. Once recovery is underway, and until the horse is cool and his thirst quenched, he can be allowed five swallows of water for every fifty metres walked.

Checking for injury

During untacking and sponging, the horse must be checked for injuries, and, once he has recovered, these can be cleaned and dressed. The horse should also be jogged for a few yards to check for soundness while he is recovering.

Care of the legs

Once the horse has cooled completely, he can return to his stable for a roll and to stale. He may appreciate a nibble of grass, but if the weather does not allow this he should have a small haynet while you attend to his legs. After a thorough check for thorns, heat and swelling, the legs can be cold-hosed or poulticed before being bandaged. The leg treatment used will vary according to personal preference, but after strenuous effort the idea is to apply a cold dressing to constrict the blood vessels and to soothe any bruising and inflammation that may be present.

The dressing, whether clay or cooling gel, should be applied thickly down the back of the leg from the knee to below the fetlock joint (43). It should then be covered in dampened newspaper, tin foil, clingfilm or plastic (44), with gamgee or another type of padding wrapped over it (45). Finally, a stable bandage is applied over the top (46).

43 Apply a thick layer of clay or gel to the leg. Rubber gloves are a good idea, as this is a messy process!

44 Cover the dressing with newspaper, tin foil, clingfilm (plastic wrap) or plastic

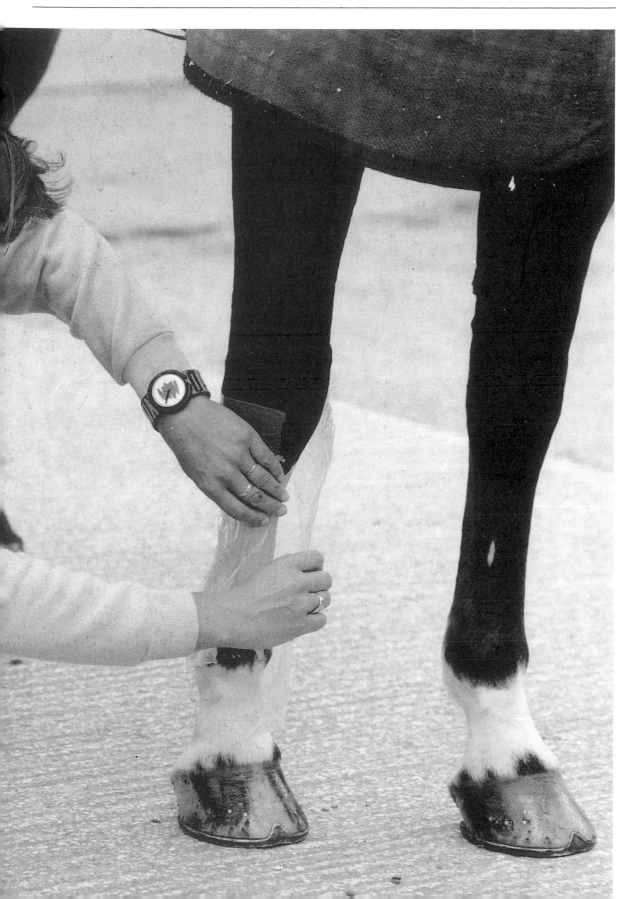

45 Place a large piece
of gamgee (sheet cotton)
or other padding over the top

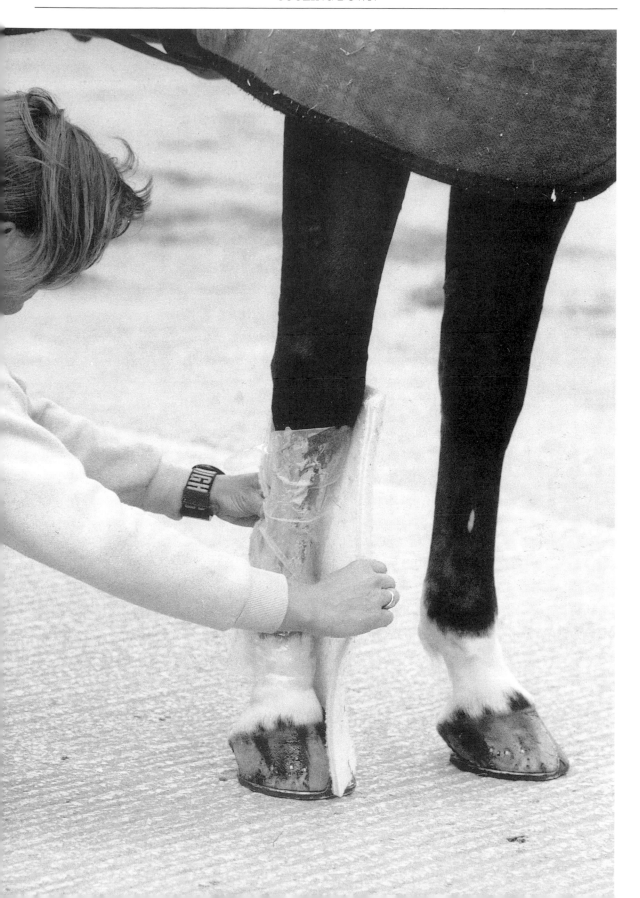

46 Wrap a stable bandage over the top to support the leg and keep the dressing in place

Further checking

Although the skin and surface muscles are cool, the horse may break out in a sweat due to heat and toxins deep in the muscles, which the body is trying to eliminate. Check the horse every fifteen minutes for cold, sweaty patches, restless behaviour, disturbed bedding or a reluctance to eat. If the signs are mild, keep the horse warm and walk him until he is dry and comfortable. If the horse does not respond or looks very distressed, veterinary help is needed.

Colic can be a problem after severe exertion, and the intestines must be kept moving. Once the horse is cool and his thirst has been quenched, he may appreciate a small bran mash, with his normal feed later on. Tired horses are easily overfaced by a large feed, but dividing the normal feed in two and feeding it at intervals may overcome this.

The horse will not have eaten for several hours which is unnatural for an animal designed to be a trickle feeder and to eat little and often. The greedy horse is as much a danger to himself as the tired horse that will not eat. Once the horse has recovered and been bandaged, rugged and returned to his stable he should be given a small haynet along with the mash or small feed mentioned above. The horse should then be left in peace and discreetly checked without disturbing him. A couple of hours later he can have another small haynet and half his normal feed. Finally the horse can be given the second half of his feed and a night time hay net. The hay or dust free alternative should be the best that you can get and it is really more important that he eats bulk rather than concentrates – carrots and sugar beet pulp may be a useful way to tempt him to eat. If the horse is eating hay and drinking water happily but refusing to eat his feed and you are worried that he may not be getting the electrolytes he needs, syringe a solu-

---

SIGNS OF OVER-STRESS

Watch the horse carefully for any of the following signs of over-stress:

- heat, swelling and pain indicating injury
- abnormal behaviour
- muscle shaking
- increased pulse and respiration rates
- reluctance to eat or drink

How to reduce stress:
- warm up the horse properly
- assess the horse and judge the pace accordingly: winning is nothing if the horse suffers
- use rests and breaks intelligently
- keep the routine and feeding as normal as possible
- transport the horse carefully
- ensure the horse is fit enough to compete
- avoid heatstroke and dehydration by providing water correctly and using electrolytes when necessary
- cool the horse correctly
- monitor recovery using temperature, pulse and respiration rates
- check for injury and care for the legs
- if in doubt call the vet

---

tion of electrolytes directly into his mouth.

If the horse has had a fall or competed under difficult conditions so that his recovery rate was slow then he should be checked through the night. Some competitors like to walk their horse to relieve any stiffness just before the late night feed. If the horse is stiff and bruised he may need intensive therapy, this may be a combination of attention from the veterinary surgeon and the equine sports therapist. The idea is twofold; to alleviate pain and to stop the horse suffering any longterm effects and, more immediately, to ensure the horse passes the final trot up prior to the last days show jumping.

10
THE
NEXT DAY

Depending on the discipline, the day after the horse has worked may be a rest and recovery day, the final day of a three-day event, or another day's show jumping or dressage.

The eventer and endurance horse may be very stiff and tired the next day, and it is your job, even if you are not competing again for a while, to turn this stiff horse into a supple athlete that is ready to run as soon as possible. In most competitions run under International Equestrian Federation (F.E.I.) rules, the use of anti-inflammatory painkillers such as phenylbutazone is banned, and without chemical aids to relieve inflammation and disguise lameness, good post-competition care is imperative. Cold hosing or the use of a water boot **(fig. 52)**, and cold poulticing, will help to reduce bruising and inflammation, while heat lamps, massage and walking will relieve stiffness.

The tired horse must be kept warm and be exposed to as little stress as possible. Just like us, horses are much more susceptible to illness and feel the cold more when they are tired, and this will be exacerbated if the horse is too tired to eat. The horse's appetite will tell you how tired he is; until he is eating up normally, he has not really recovered from his exertions

and should be allowed plenty of rest. Hacks and grazing in hand will help the horse to relax and recover. Tempt him to eat using succulents such as carrots and sugar beet pulp and ensure that he is fed the best quality hay or dust-free alternative.

Fig. 52 An alternative to cold hosing is a simple water boot, which attaches to the hosepipe so that a spray of water runs down the horse's leg

Equine sports therapy

The physiotherapist and equine sports therapist are now an important part of the team that manages the equine athlete, helping him to fulfil his performance potential and also promoting effective recovery from injury and exertion. No football team would travel without their 'physio', and it is now common to see a horse's physio working on him the night after the cross-country of a three-day event.

When correctly used, physiotherapy provides a complete regime for the horse – from preventive care, through the instigation of a treatment regime, to rehabilitation techniques – which will maximize performance. No injury or loss in performance should be ignored, and the sooner the problem is treated, the more satisfactory the end result will be. Nature alone will not allow the maximum performance to be achieved, as there may be restricted mobility, loss of full power and decreased function.

Techniques for treating injury

Most of the machinery that is used in sports therapy is readily obtainable, but, unfortunately, incorrect use of this equipment can be very harmful. The horse owner should only use therapeutic machines with the guidance of skilled and trained therapists or veterinary surgeons. Do not assume that, because one technique worked for a certain injury, the same technique is suitable for a different type of problem. Remember too that, even though a horse may now be sound, the injury may not be completely healed.

Fig. 53 Whirlpool boots being used to cool and massage the horse's legs

Hot and cold treatment

The application of cold will help to control the inflammatory reaction and to relieve pain. The cold treatment should be applied frequently for short periods of time, and may take the form of proprietary cold dressings and bandages, a bag of frozen peas or whirlpool boots, which also have a massaging, jacuzzi effect **(fig. 53)**. Once the initial, acute phase of the injury has passed, hot and cold therapies can be alternated to increase the blood flow to the affected area, bringing with it the elements essential for healing. These treatments will ease the stiff horse, allowing him to rest more effectively.

Massage and passive stretching

Massage and soft-tissue manipulation are used extensively by human athletes, both routinely during training and before and after strenuous exercise, to ensure that everything is functioning properly. Skilled massage is a very valuable area of physiotherapy, and can effectively relieve pain and increase blood flow to an area, accomplishing the same aim as all the expensive therapeutic machinery.

Massage can be used for muscle stiffness and spasms, filled legs and soft-tissue problems. The underlying tissue is massaged with either a linear or circular movement with the fingers, or by direct compression using the heel of the hand. Massage leads to friction which heats the skin and underlying tissues as they move over each other, dilates the blood vessels and improves the circulation from deeper tissues to these more superficial parts.

Passive-stretching exercises can be used to move the horse's limbs through their normal range, to stretch the muscles and flex the joints (see **47** overleaf). This can be useful before working the horse or trotting him up for soundness.

Mechanical massage

Mechanical-massage machines utilize a number of techniques including laser, ultrasound, magnetic field and muscle stimulation.

Laser therapy Two main types of therapeutic laser are on sale to the general public: one which produces a visible red beam, and another which emits an invisible beam. Laser treatments can be as short as one minute, but are usually longer. Be sure to read the instructions, and never over-treat. Lasers can also be used to perform acupuncture, stimulating the acupuncture points rather than directly treating the affected area.

The relief of pain is an important attribute of laser treatment, and may be better than giving painkilling drugs. Lasers can, however, ease pain to such an extent that the rider thinks that the horse has recovered sufficiently to start work or to have work levels increased, even though healing may not be complete, and so more damage will be done. Laser can be used to treat tendon and ligament injuries, superficial bone and joint injuries, open wounds and old fibrous injuries. In the case of open wounds, prompt use of a laser has been found to accelerate healing without the formation of proud flesh, but laser therapy should never be started until a veterinary diagnosis has been obtained. If the wrong ailment is being treated, the horse may suffer.

Ultrasound Ultrasound therapy can be one of the most effective forms of treatment, and has produced outstanding results at the initial stages of repair. Ultrasound can reduce muscle spasm, increase the elasticity of scar tissue, stimulate blood circulation and cellular activity and improve the quality of tendon repair, providing that treatment is given

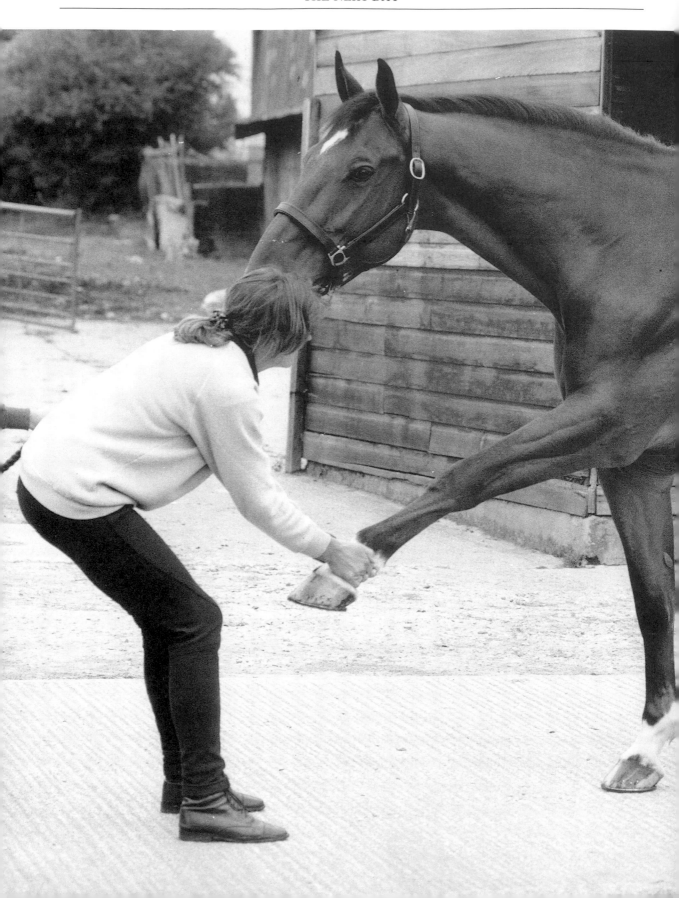

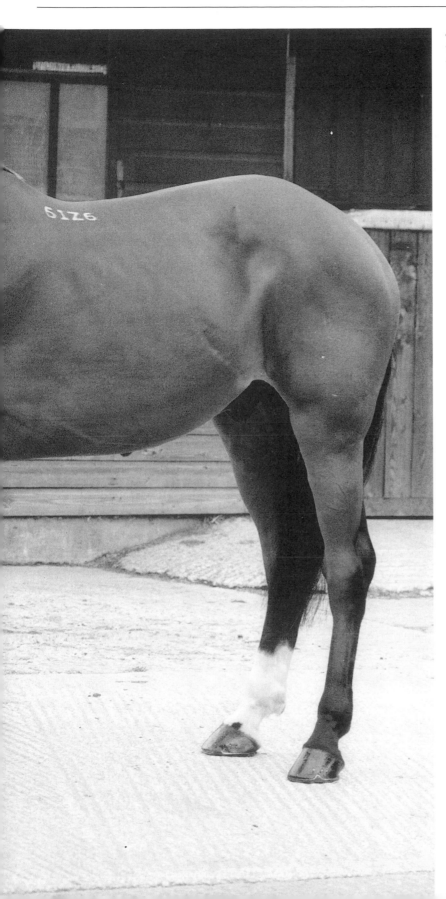

47 Passive exercise can be used to stretch the muscles and flex the joints

in the two weeks immediately after injury. The use of ultrasound should be limited to specific injuries, after consultation with a veterinary surgeon or qualified equine therapist.

Magnetic-field therapy Magnetic-field therapy (M.F.T.) is another form of treatment whose effects on tissue are far from being sufficiently understood or researched. M.F.T. can be useful for bruising fractures and for joint and ligament injuries. Magnetic foil pads and boots can be used to treat minor problems quite safely, and may well justify a place in the competition horse's first-aid box. Machines which provide pulsed or static magnetic-field therapy should be used under the supervision of an expert, and the manufacturer's instructions and suggested treatment times should be carefully observed.

Large machines are available which use a pulsing magnetic field. This is set up around the area to be treated by adaptors, which may be held in position by velcro pads on cotton sheets. The magnetic field increases the blood circulation in superficial tissue, and this has an effect on deeper tissues.

Electro-vet and Ionicare Electro-vet and Ionicare are similar systems, and are useful for treating bruising, filled joints, windgalls and mild muscle weakness (in the USA, you should consult your veterinary surgeon about the similar treatments and methods that are available). When an injury occurs, the ion charge of surrounding normal cells becomes electrically out of balance, which inhibits the function of the cells. As electrotherapy has become increasingly understood, it has been suggested that a low-frequency current passing through the tissue influences the cells and allows them to resume their normal function.

TRAVELLING HOME AND THE NEXT FEW DAYS

- Although the competition has finished, and everyone is tired, you must ensure that the horse is cared for as well on the way home as he was on the way to the competition. Remember that travelling can be stressful for a horse – in fact, he is more likely to be stressed on the way home because he is tired.

- The three or four days after a strenuous competition are very important to the horse's well-being. He will be feeling low, and any damage that did not show up immediately will start to make its appearance. The horse will have been living on adrenalin during the competition, and, as he lets down and relaxes, he will start to feel the aches and pains.

- Keep the horse in light work rather than turning him out in the field to stiffen up: walking exercise will prevent adhesions forming in muscles and give the horse time to wind down a little.

- Once the horse's attitude tells you that he has recovered from the competition, he can either be roughed off for his well-deserved rest, or return to his fitness programme and be prepared for the next competition (see **48** on pages 158–9).

- The horses work load will have dropped dramatically and so his feeding regime must also change. He will need a certain amount of concentrate feed to replace lost body reserves, however this is likely to be about half his previous concentrate ration.

- Tempt him to eat using succulents such as carrots and sugar beet pulp.

- Ensure that he is fed as much of the best quality hay or dust-free alternative that he wants

- Now is the time to sort out any lameness problems, they are unlikely to go away in the field. Many therapy machines are available for hire or purchase but they should only be used under expert supervision. Consult your veterinary surgeon who will refer you to a suitably qualified therapist.

11
KEEPING THE COMPETITION HORSE FIT

One of the most skilful areas of competition-horse care is keeping the horse fit for prolonged periods. Training for one competition is not too difficult, but to keep the horse fit, fresh and sound for a season of competition is much more demanding.

Once the horse is fit and competing regularly, it is important not to over-work and over-train him. The routine should be varied to suit the individual horse, depending on the frequency and level of competition. The type and amount of work that a horse needs will also depend on his breeding, temperament, conformation and whether he has any soundness problems. You need to assess your horse as an individual to find out what will suit him best. Try not to get your horse too fit: it will not do him any good, mentally or physically. If he does go 'over the top', turn him out in the field for a couple of days to help him to relax, and with any luck you will find him much easier to ride!

One way of preventing a horse from becoming 'stale' is to vary the type of work that you give him. Alternative methods of exercise include swimming **(fig. 54)**, water walks, treadmills and horse walkers.

Fig. 54 Swimming for fitness

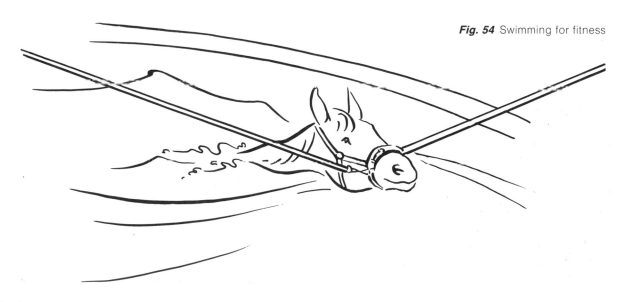

Swimming

Swimming can be a very useful part of a training programme. Horses which need to maintain fitness but are temporarily lame, those which cannot withstand the stress of a hard, traditional training regime and those suffering from the effects of wear will all benefit from swimming.

The absence of weight on the limbs means that movement underwater is less painful, and that joints can move freely through their full range of action. If a joint does not move, it will deteriorate and become a problem, even if it was not the original cause of lameness. A horse in pain will develop uneven musculature as he compensates to save the area that hurts. Swimming will keep the muscles in use and help to build balanced muscles, which may even adjust uneven action.

A horse on box rest cannot get rid of his surplus energy, and, when brought back to work, may well become over-excited and damage unfit muscles. Swimming during the recovery period will exercise the horse and maintain his muscle tone.

Stale or over-trained horses and horses with psychological difficulties have all benefited from swimming, and it can be included in the training programmes of horses as diverse as racehorses and police horses.

Swimming as part of a fitness programme

The horse should only swim for a short time initially, and must learn to swim correctly. If he is tired or frightened, he will be tense, and will swim with tight muscles and poor technique. Heart rates should be taken before and after swimming and the horse's recovery noted, just as in an interval-training programme. In this way, the horse's workload can be built up gradually to produce the best results.

Once the horse is used to swimming he will swim with a heart rate of between 140 and 170 beats per minute; this is equivalent to a 500 m.p.m. canter and forms very useful aerobic exercise. This means that three three-minute swims can replace one canter session from week nine of the training programme onward (see page 33). As with canter work, the horse should be allowed to recover until his heart rate falls below 100 b.p.m. before being asked to perform the next period of swimming. After the swim, the horse should be scraped as dry as possible, have a cooler thrown over him and be walked until he is dry (this will take at least fifteen minutes).

Anaerobic work with heart rates over 200 b.p.m. can be achieved by using tethered or restricted swimming, and should only be carried out for short periods. If the horse is made to swim for short periods at varying speeds with short recovery times, he will develop muscles for work, not just for keeping him afloat.

Water walks

Swimming is sometimes criticised as being artificial, and only teaching a horse to win swimming races! Water walks provide good exercise and remedial treatment. Walking is good exercise in itself, and walking through water is harder work, with the advantage of reduced concussion and cushioning while still bearing weight.

Just like any other form of exercise the duration of exercise in the water walk has to be built up gradually and is often done in an interval training manner, with the horse being allowed to partially recover in between repeated sessions in the water walk.

Horse walkers

Horse walkers are great time-savers. The most sophisticated models can be programmed for walk and trot on both reins for specified times. All horses benefit from walking work during their exercise programme, either to warm up prior to work, or to cool down thoroughly after work, yet many people are short of time and inevitably this is the part that gets skimped. In a large yard a horse walker can help to overcome this problem, although it should not be used as a substitute for ridden work. Horses can be exercised on the walker in schooling tack such as a chambon but the horse must be supervised and worked correctly. Wearing tack keeps the saddle and girth area hard.

Profiling the competition horse

The amount and type of work that a horse needs to keep him fit throughout the competition season will depend on his make and shape, as well as the type of work that he is doing. Stuffy horses need more fast work than their longer-striding counterparts, for instance, while some dressage horses or show jumpers may need specific exercises to keep them supple and athletic. We can assess what type of exercise our horse needs by drawing up a profile.

We all have a picture of the ideal equine athlete for our chosen discipline, in terms of conformation, movement and temperament. Unless we are very lucky, it is unlikely that our own horse conforms to this ideal, and this is where building a

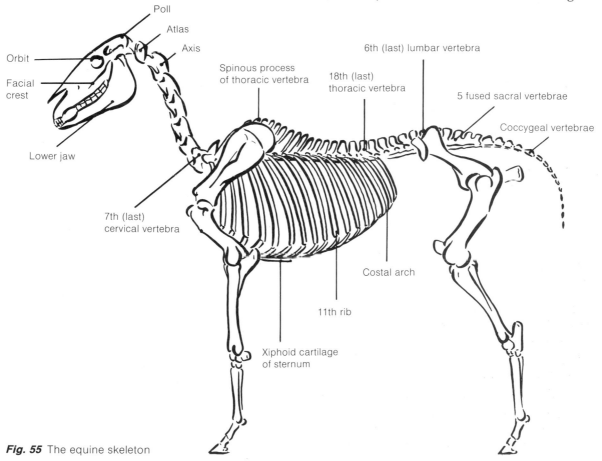

Fig. 55 The equine skeleton

profile can prove useful. The idea is to consider how closely our horse conforms to the ideal, noting his good points and his weak points; the weak points will limit the horse's performance and may even be areas susceptible to injury. Our assessment of the horse can then be used to train and develop him to make the most of his good points and to strengthen the weak ones. This will protect him from wear and tear, and will also help to maximize his athletic performance. There are many areas of assessment to include in the profile. It is, essentially, your horse condensed on to paper, and contains his history, description, measurements and assessments. The assessments include:

- skeletal measurement
- muscular development
- hoof balance
- movement and action
- temperament
- mouth assessment
- condition

Conformation consists of two aspects: the skeleton and the muscles, and the fat and skin that clothe them. The skeleton is the framework of the horse and is unlikely to alter after maturity except through injury or neglect (see **fig. 55** on the previous page). The developed shape of the horse depends on the muscles and fat which give the horse his shape and posture, and these aspects will depend on how the horse has been cared for and worked. The horse may have a skeleton that is less than perfectly proportioned and yet appear to have a perfect shape, because his planned development programme has compensated for the imperfection. On the other hand, the neglected, poorly developed horse may have good skeletal conformation and yet not look like a show horse. The successful producer of show horses has to have X-ray eyes and the ability to imagine how the horse in the rough will look after a development programme!

Skeletal conformation

Remember that you are evaluating the whole horse, so that, for example, if the horse has a large head, this may upset his balance unless he has a good strong neck – perhaps slightly shorter than normal – to support it. We are also concerned with balance and proportion: a racehorse's balance must be at its optimum when the horse is galloping, while a dressage horse must balance best at the slower, more collected movements.

The length of a horse's back will determine his ability to carry weight. The horse was not designed to carry weight on top of his back, but to carry his huge gut in suspension, and carrying a rider stresses the horse's back muscles and vertebrae. Extra length will increase that stress, so we look for a short, strong back with a long croup which can accommodate a good muscle mass. The more weight that the horse has to carry, the greater the girth measurement should be, as this will help to support and compensate for a slightly long back. The heart and lungs are also housed here and need plenty of room.

The horse's wither height should be about the same as his length. A hunter with an excess of length over height will tire more quickly, while a dressage horse that is taller than he is long will have a short base of support, and, when he is asked to perform collected movements, this will shorten even further. If the horse is croup-high, he will give a downhill ride with more weight on his forehand, making gymnastic work difficult. If this is not too pronounced, he can be trained to elevate the forehand and lower his croup, but there may always be a problem.

If the attachment of the head to the neck is thick, the horse will find it difficult to flex his poll and relax his jaw comfortably, so he will resist collection and develop short, bulging muscle. The way in which the neck is set on to the withers is also an important consideration. A low-set neck will give good stride length to the galloping racehorse, while the dressage horse will need a higher-set neck to achieve elevation.

Mouth assessment

The horse's mouth is a very sensitive area, and should be assessed carefully at regular intervals. You should look for sharp edges on the molar teeth, and for the eruption of wolf teeth in young horses. It is equally important to observe the size and shape of the horse's mouth, as this will determine the best type of bit for the horse. Factors such as the ability of the rider, the type of activity and the stage of the horse's training will also affect your choice of bit.

The feet

Measuring the angle made by the hoof and pastern, the height of the hoof wall at the heels and toes, and the rate of growth of the horse's feet will tell you about gradual changes inside the hoof that are not noticed on a day-to-day basis **(fig. 56)**. These measurements will be an aid to indicate to your vet or farrier what is wrong if your horse goes lame. Regular trimming and shoeing will help to improve hoof balance and shape. A balanced hoof is fundamental to keeping horses sound, and the long-toe/low-heel conformation seen so often is known to contribute to tendon and ligament problems. The heel should be approximately half the height of the toe, any less and it is said to be collapsed.

Fig. 56 The ideal angles of a balanced foot

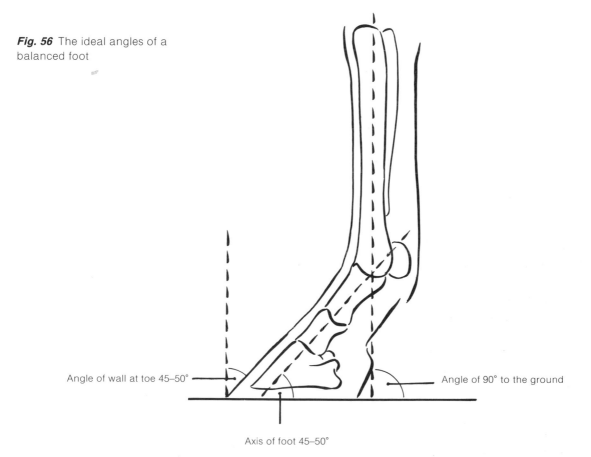

Angle of wall at toe 45–50°

Angle of 90° to the ground

Axis of foot 45–50°

Movement and action

If the horse does not move his limbs straight, or places his feet on the ground unevenly, this will place strain on the muscles, tendons and ligaments, and may eventually lead to lameness (figs. 57 and 58). Some horses move so badly that one limb may strike or interfere with another (fig. 59). Observe the paths and directions that the feet follow, the flight and elevation of each limb and how the feet are placed on the ground. Careful observation followed by discussion with your farrier may help.

Many successful horses do not move straight or have limbs that are slightly crooked in their alignment; providing that you are aware of the horse's deficiencies and take account of them in your development programme soundness problems may be avoided. It is important to protect the

horses limbs using appropriate boots, generally speaking horses should wear brushing boots all round for schooling, open-fronted tendon boots and coronet boots for show jumping and strong, supportive leg protection all round for fast work or cross country.

Even if not perfectly straight in his movement, look for a horse that remains balanced at all times, even when ridden round corners. The walk should have a true four time rhythm with a good length of stride; it must not be hurried. Ideally all the paces should give the impression that the horse is able to 'sit' and bring his hindquarters underneath him, giving a smooth flowing and elastic movement. Some dressage trainers choose a horse on the walk and canter as these paces are the most difficult to improve and remember this is the pace the eventer and show jumper have to jump out of.

Fig. 57 'Dishing' from the shoulder

Fig. 58 'Turning a toe' from the knee

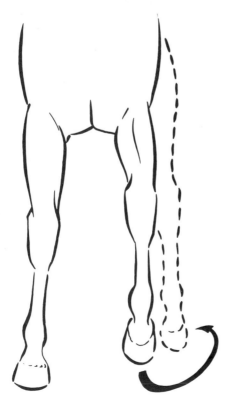

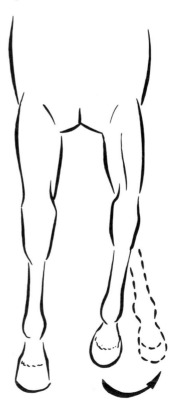

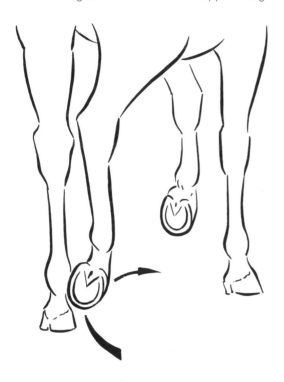

Fig. 59 The horse moves too close behind, so that the foot brushes against the fetlock of the opposite leg

Designing a development programme

To carry a rider efficiently, the horse must be developed to carry himself properly. Firstly, his balance must be developed, and then the carrying capacity of the hindquarters increased so that the joints can flex effectively to produce power. Once the hindquarters are engaged, the forehand will be able to lighten.

Whatever discipline your horse is competing in, his preparation should include basic work to improve his balance and posture, taking into account his individual shape as detailed in his profile. The horse should be encouraged to stretch his top line and to raise his bottom line, thus developing the abdominal muscles. If the abdominals are weak, the horse will not be able to lift his gut, round his back or engage his quarters.

The development work aims to enable the horse to carry your weight economically, and without compromising his athletic ability. The important aspects to develop are:

- the balancing of body weight
- the length and power of the stride
- the weight-carrying capacity
- athletic dexterity

USING PHYSIOLOGY TO GET HORSES FITTER

- As we learn more about the exercising horse and how he functions, and as the equine sports therapist becomes accepted as an important member of the performance horse's team, we see that the therapist has a role in getting the horse fit, as well as helping him to recover from injury.
- Centres now specialize in pre-conditioning therapy to help the horse withstand the stress of a training programme. This pre-season training is designed to stimulate the horse's metabolism, so that, when he is asked to work, he can co-ordinate and balance his muscular activity and internal body processes.
- This therapy aims, for example, to stimulate the circulation of blood through the tissues through the use of electro-medical therapy, such as ultrasound, faradism and electro-magnetic therapy. The idea is that, when the horse goes into his conventional training programme and the muscles demand oxygen for energy production, the pre-conditioned circulation will be able to respond correctly, thus avoiding injury.

APPENDIX
AND INDEX

APPENDIX

Equipment to be taken to a competition when staying overnight

- Stable tools, skip, muck sack
- Shavings or paper
- Two haynets
- Two water buckets and water carrier
- Feed bowl
- Pre-packed and labelled concentrate feed
- Hay or haylage
- Supplements (e.g., electrolytes)
- Water from home for fussy drinkers
- Grooming kit, including extra sponges, towels, sweat scraper, hoof oil and fly spray
- Plaiting kit
- Spare set of shoes, studs and fitting kit
- Tack-cleaning kit
- Spare rugs and blankets
- Two sweat sheets or coolers
- Waterproof rugs
- Stable bandages and gamgee (sheet cotton), or wraps
- Passport/vaccination certificate

Other essential items

- Tack (depending on the horse and competition)

- Bandages, brushing boots, over-reach boots (plus spares)
- Spare girth, leathers, stirrups and reins
- Spare headcollar (halter) and rope
- Lungeing equipment
- Travelling equipment for horse
- Human first-aid kit
- Equine first-aid kit, to include scissors, cotton wool, crêpe bandages, gamgee, salt, wound dressings and sprays, ready-to-use poultice, leg coolant

Equipment to be taken to a three-day event

Tack

- Bridles for dressage, cross-country and show jumping
- Spare bridle
- Selection of bits
- Bootlace to tie bridle to plait on cross-country
- Martingale (plus spare)
- Breastplate/breastgirth (plus spare)
- Spare rubber reins and stops
- Dressage saddle, girth, leathers and stirrups

- Jumping saddle, girth (plus spare), leathers and stirrups
- Overgirth (plus spare)
- Weightcloth and lead
- Saddlecloths and numnahs (saddle-pads), both for work and competition
- Spare leathers and stirrups
- Lungeing cavesson
- Lunge whip
- Side reins
- Best headcollar (halter) and lead rope
- Spare headcollar (halter) and lead rope
- Bridle hook and saddle horse
- Tack-cleaning equipment
- Metal polish
- Hole punch

Boots and bandages

- Over-reach boots (plus spares)
- Front and back exercise boots
- Boots and/or bandages for cross-country
- Boots and/or bandages for show jumping
- Spare cross-country boots (front and back)
- Tail bandages
- Travelling bandages/boots
- Stable bandages
- Gamgee (sheet cotton) or wraps
- Poultice and bandages
- Clingfilm (plastic wrap)
- Talcum powder
- Pins, tape, needle and thread

Rugs

- Night blankets
- Two anti-sweat sheets
- Cotton sheet
- Waterproof sheet
- Quarter sheet
- Best day rug
- Rollers/surcingles

Washing-down equipment

- Buckets
- Sponges and shampoo
- Sweat scraper
- Towels
- Water container

Stud box

- Spare shoes
- Assortment of studs
- Tap
- Spanner (pliers)/wrench
- Nails
- Cotton wool and oil
- Farrier's tools
- Hoof pick
- Equiboot (Easyboot)

Feed

- Feed and water buckets
- Feed and hay/haylage
- Scoop
- Supplements and electrolytes
- Haynets

Stable tools

- Bedding
- Skip, fork, shovel, broom
- Disinfectant
- Tool box

Grooming kit

- Grooming kit
- Headcollar (halter) and rope
- Fly spray
- Hoof dressing and hoof pick
- Plaiting equipment
- Clippers, extension, circuit breaker and oil, spare blades
- Twitch
- Grease
- Detergent

- Leg poultices and cooling agents
- Thermometer
- Scissors
- Torch (flashlight)

Equine first-aid kit

- Thermometer
- Non-adherent pads and gamgee (sheet cotton)
- Crêpe bandages, tape and pins
- Sticking plaster (adhesive tape)
- Cotton wool
- Instant ice pack
- Scissors and tweezers
- Small metal bowl
- Syringe for cleaning wounds
- Wound cream and powder
- Antiseptic for cleaning wounds
- Epsom salts
- Witch hazel
- Vaseline

- A second, smaller first-aid kit should be available to take to the steeplechase

Equipment to be taken to a long distance ride

- Full 5 gallon water container
- One bucket for washing down, one bucket for drinking

- Funnel to pour unused water back into container
- Sponges, sweat scraper and towels
- Headcollar and lead rope plus spare lead rope
- Rugs including waterproof sheet and sweat rug or thermal equivalent
- Surcingle
- Spare set of shoes
- Tack plus spare reins, leathers, girth and numnah
- Equine first aid kit including bandages
- Human first aid kit
- Drink for rider
- Coat for rider
- Grooming kit
- Haynet
- Feed
- Electrolytes
- Stethoscope
- 'Slosh' bottles

While competing the rider should carry

- Folding hoof pick
- Map of route and any directions in plastic case
- Money for phone and emergency phone number
- Compass
- Card showing expected time of arrival at agreed meeting places
- String for emergency repairs
- Bandage for emergency first aid

A guide to speeds and paces

Gait	Speed km/hr	metres per minute	mph
brisk walk	6	100	3.7
slow trot	9	150	5.5
medium trot	12	200	7.5
fast trot	15	250	9.3
slow canter	21	350	13.0
medium canter	24	400	14.8
brisk canter	27	450	16.8
hand gallop	30	500	18.7
medium gallop	36	600	24.3

INDEX